Course **3**

Core-Plus Mathematics

Contemporary Mathematics in Context

2nd Edition

Unit 8
Resource Masters
Inverse Functions

James T. Fey • Christian R. Hirsch • Eric W. Hart
Harold L. Schoen • Ann E. Watkins

with

Beth E. Ritsema • Rebecca K. Walker • Sabrina Keller
Robin Marcus • Arthur F. Coxford • Gail Burrill

Mc Graw Hill **Glencoe**

Glencoe

The McGraw·Hill Companies

This material is based upon work supported, in part, by the National Science Foundation under grant no. ESI 0137718. Opinions expressed are those of the authors and not necessarily those of the Foundation.

Send all inquiries to:
The McGraw-Hill Companies
8787 Orion Place
Columbus, OH 43240-4027

ISBN: 978-0-07-890728-9   Core-Plus Mathematics
MHID: 0-07-890728-4   *Contemporary Mathematics in Context*
                             Course 3 Unit 8 Resource Masters

Printed in the United States of America.

1 2 3 4 5 6 7 8 9 10 066 17 16 15 14 13 12 11 10 09 08

Table of Contents

Teacher's Guide to Using the Unit 8 Resource Masters

Core-Plus Mathematics
Using the Unit Resource Masters

Overview of Unit Resource Masters

To assist you as you teach Course 3 of *Core-Plus Mathematics*, unit-specific resource books have been developed. The unit resources provided can help you focus student attention on the important mathematics being developed. They can be used to help students organize their results related to specific problems, synthesize what they are learning, and practice for standardized tests.

Unit resource books provide the following types of masters in the order that they are used in the unit.
- *Transparency Masters*
  1. Think About This Situation (TATS) masters to help launch the lesson
  2. Masters to collect class results
  3. Summarize the Mathematics (STM) masters to help facilitate the synthesis of mathematical ideas from the investigation (To guide your planning, sample discussion scenarios called "Promoting Mathematical Discourse" are provided in the Teacher's Guide for selected TATS and STM discussions.)

- *Student Masters*
  1. Masters to help students organize or display their results or thinking.
  2. Masters to help students develop their proof-writing abilities (differentiation)
  3. Technology Tips to facilitate learning technology features of graphing calculators, *CPMP-Tools* software, and computer algebra systems (CAS)
  4. Templates for manipulatives
  5. Unit Summary masters to provide a starting point for pulling together the main mathematical ideas of a unit
  6. Practicing for Standardized Tests masters provide an opportunity for students to complete tasks presented in the format of most high-stakes tests and to consider test-taking strategies. (Solutions to these tasks are printed in the Teacher's Guide following the final unit Summarize the Mathematics. This allows you the option of providing or not providing the solutions to students.)

- *Assessment Masters*
  1. Quizzes (two forms for each lesson)
  2. In-class tests (two forms for each unit)
  3. Take-home assessment items (three items for each unit)
  4. Projects (two for each unit except Unit 1)
  5. Midterm and end-of-course assessment items (Unit 4 and Unit 8 contain a bank of assessment items from which to design cumulative exams.)

All of the items in this book are included for viewing and printing from the *Core-Plus Mathematics* TeacherWorks Plus CD-ROM. Custom tailoring of assessment items in this book, as well as creation of additional items, can be accomplished by using the ExamView Assessment Suite.

Assessment in Core-Plus Mathematics

Throughout the *Core-Plus Mathematics* curriculum, the term "assessment" is meant to include all instances of gathering information about students' levels of understanding and their disposition toward mathematics for purposes of making decisions about instruction. The dimensions of student performance that are assessed in this curriculum (see chart below) are consistent with the assessment recommendations of the National Council of Teachers of Mathematics in the *Assessment Standards for School Mathematics* (NCTM, 1995). They are more comprehensive than those of a typical testing program.

Assessment Dimensions		
Process	**Content**	**Disposition**
Problem Solving	Concepts	Beliefs
Reasoning	Applications	Perseverance
Communication	Representational Strategies	Confidence
Connections	Procedures	Enthusiasm

These unit resource masters contain the tools for formal assessment of the process and content dimensions of student performance. Calculators are assumed in most cases on these assessments. Teacher discretion should be used regarding student access to their textbooks and Math Toolkits for assessments. In general, if the goals to be assessed are problem solving and reasoning, while memory of facts and procedural skill are of less interest, resources should be allowed. However, if automaticity of procedures or unaided recall are being assessed, it is appropriate to prohibit resource materials.

You may want to consult the extended section on assessment in the front matter of the Course 3 *Core-Plus Mathematics Teacher's Guide* and *Implementing Core-Plus Mathematics*. Among the topics presented in these sources are curriculum-embedded assessment, student-generated assessment, and scoring assessments and assigning grades. Since the *Core-Plus Mathematics* approach and materials provide a wide variety of assessment information, the teacher will be in a good position to assign grades. With such a wide choice of assessment opportunities, a word of caution is appropriate: *It is easy to overassess students, and care must be taken to avoid doing so.* Since many rich opportunities for assessing students are embedded in the curriculum itself, you may choose not to use a quiz at the end of every lesson or to replace all or portions of an in-class test with take-home tasks or projects.

Think About This Situation

The challenge of sending clear text messages is finding a way to translate letters into numbers so that the receiver can translate those numbers back into the intended letters. One popular procedure for text message coding, called *predictive text*, asks the sender to simply press numbers that correspond to desired letters.

a How do you think a cell phone using the predictive text procedure determines intended words from number sequences?

b Suppose that a text message is entered by pressing 4, 6, 6, 3, 2, 2, 5, 5. What do you think was the intended message?

A Coding Method
Problem 2

2. To avoid the problems that can occur when several letters are assigned the same numerical code on a cell phone keypad, information systems, like those used by computers, employ more than ten numbers to code the letters of the alphabet and important symbols. For example, a coding scheme might make the assignments in the next tables.

Symbol	0	1	2	3	4	5	6	7	8	9	A	B	C
Code	0	1	2	3	4	5	6	7	8	9	10	11	12

Symbol	D	E	F	G	H	I	J	K	L	M	N	O	P
Code	13	14	15	16	17	18	19	20	21	22	23	24	25

Symbol	Q	R	S	T	U	V	W	X	Y	Z	.	—
Code	26	27	28	29	30	31	32	33	34	35	36	37

a. Using this coding scheme, what message is implied by the sequence of code numbers 22, 14, 14, 29, 37, 22, 14, 37, 10, 29, 37, 9?

b. Why does this coding scheme involve very low risk of incorrect message transmission?

c. If you want a message to be sent so that only the intended recipient can read it, why will a simple code like that shown in the table *not* be effective?

Copyright © Glencoe/McGraw-Hill, a division of The McGraw-Hill Companies, Inc.

Student Master • *use with page 540*

Summarize
the Mathematics

In this investigation, you compared several encryption procedures to reveal properties of schemes that provide accurate and difficult-to-break message-coding methods. The methods you examined were:

(1) the assignment of number codes to letters by cell phone buttons.

(2) the assignment of number codes to digits, letters, periods, and spaces as in $0 \rightarrow 0, 1 \rightarrow 1, \ldots, A \rightarrow 10, B \rightarrow 11, \ldots, Z \rightarrow 35, . \rightarrow 36, — \rightarrow 37$.

(3) the algorithm that encrypted numbers with the function $f(x) = x + 16$.

(4) the algorithm that encrypted numbers with the function $g(x) = 2x + 1$.

(5) the algorithm that encrypted numbers with the function $h(x) = x^2$.

(6) the algorithm that encrypted numbers with the function $k(x) = 38x - x^2$.

(7) the algorithm that encrypted number blocks by multiplication with $C = \begin{bmatrix} 2 & 1 \\ 5 & 3 \end{bmatrix}$.

Summarize the Mathematics Cont.

a Which of the coding and encryption functions assigns code numbers to message letters and numbers in ways that can always be decoded to accurately retrieve the intended message? For the methods that do *not* decode accurately, explain why not.

b What properties of a coding function f will guarantee that messages encrypted by that function can always be decoded accurately?

Be prepared to explain your ideas to the class.

Strategies for Finding Inverses
Problem 7

7. Finding inverses (when they exist) for nonlinear functions is generally more challenging than for linear functions. Study the following strategies for finding the inverse of $f(x) = \dfrac{5}{x-2}$ to see if you agree that they are both correct.

Strategy I	**Strategy II**
If $\qquad y = \dfrac{5}{x-2}$	If $\qquad y = \dfrac{5}{x-2}$
Then $\quad y(x-2) = 5$	Swap the roles of y and x to get
Then $\quad x - 2 = \dfrac{5}{y}$	$x = \dfrac{5}{y-2}$
Then $\quad x = \dfrac{5}{y} + 2$	Then $y - 2 = \dfrac{5}{x}$
So, $\qquad f^{-1}(x) = \dfrac{5}{x} + 2.$	Then $f^{-1}(x) = \dfrac{5}{x} + 2.$

Adapt one strategy or the other to find rules for inverses of the following functions.

a. If $g(x) = \dfrac{7}{x} + 4$, then $g^{-1}(x) = \dots$.

b. If $h(x) = \dfrac{7}{x+4}$, then $h^{-1}(x) = \dots$.

c. If $j(x) = \dfrac{7}{x}$, then $j^{-1}(x) = \dots$.

b. If $k(x) = x^2$ $(x \geq 0)$, then $k^{-1}(x) = \dots$.

Finding Inverse Functions
Problem 8

8. In some situations, you will need to find the inverse of a function that is defined only by a table of values or a graph.

   a. Suppose that assignments of the function $f(x)$ are as shown in the following table. Make a similar table that shows the assignments made by $f^{-1}(x)$. Then describe the domain and range of $f(x)$ and $f^{-1}(x)$.

x	−4	−3	−2	−1	0	1	2	3	4
f(x)	2	1	0	−1	−2	−3	−4	−5	−6
f⁻¹(x)									

   b. Suppose that the assignments of the function $g(x)$ are as shown on the graph below.

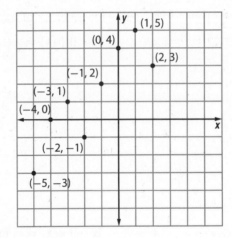

   i. On the graph above, plot points that represent assignments made by $g^{-1}(x)$. Then describe the domain and range of $g(x)$ and $g^{-1}(x)$.

   ii. Draw line segments connecting each point (a, b) on the graph of $g(x)$ to the corresponding point (b, a) on the graph of $g^{-1}(x)$. Then describe the pattern that seems to relate corresponding points on the graphs of $g(x)$ and $g^{-1}(x)$.

Summarize the Mathematics

In this investigation, you explored properties of functions that guarantee existence of inverses and strategies for finding rules for those inverses. You also explored how the graphs of a function and its inverse are related geometrically.

a What patterns in an arrow diagram or coordinate graph for a function indicate that the function does or does not have an inverse?

b What strategies are helpful in finding the rule for f^{-1} when you know the rule for f?

c What geometric pattern relates graphs of functions and their inverses?

Be prepared to explain your ideas to the class.

Check Your Understanding

Use your understanding of functions and their inverses to complete the following tasks.

a. Draw arrows on the next diagram to illustrate image variable assignments made by the function $f(x) = -x$. Then explain how the pattern of those arrows suggests that the function does or does not have an inverse.

$$f(x) = -x$$

b. Which of the graphs below show functions that have inverses? Justify your response.

Graph I $f(x) = 0.5^x - 4$

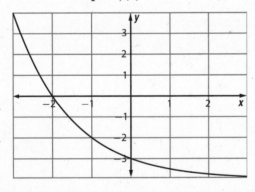

Graph II $g(x) = \sin x$

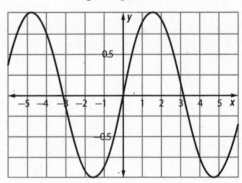

c. Find algebraic rules for the inverses of the following functions.

  i. $f(x) = 0.5x - 2$

  ii. $g(x) = \dfrac{0.5}{x} - 2$

Name _____

Date _____

LESSON 1 QUIZ

Form A

1. In this lesson, you learned that not all functions have inverses.

   a. Provide an equation for a function that does not have an inverse. Explain why the function does not have an inverse.

   b. How can you use the graph of a function to determine whether or not the function has an inverse?

2. The area of a circle is a function of the radius of the circle.

   a. Does this function have an inverse? Explain your reasoning.

   b. Explain what the inverse function will tell you about the variables in the situation.

3. The amount of time (in hours) it will take to prepare a mass mailing of a newsletter when there are x people working on the job is determined by the equation $f(x) = \frac{12}{x} + 1$.

    a. Find $f(2)$ and explain its meaning in this situation.

    b. $f^{-1}(3) = 6$. Explain what this tells you about the situation.

    c. Find a formula for $f^{-1}(x)$.

4. Find an algebraic rule for the inverse of each function.

    a. $y = 4x + 9$

    b. $y = \frac{2x - 5}{7}$

LESSON 1 QUIZ

Form A
Suggested Solutions

1. **a.** Function equations will vary. The explanation should provide specific examples of two different x values that produce the same y value and a statement that this implies that there would be an x value of the inverse that would be associated with two different y values. This means that the inverse would not be a function.

    b. If you can draw two different points on the graph of the function that have the same y value, the function will not have an inverse.

2. **a.** Yes, this function does have an inverse. For every area, there is only one radius that will give that area.

    b. The inverse function will tell you what the radius of a circle must be in order to get a given area.

3. **a.** $f(2) = 7$. This tells us that if there are two people working on preparing the mailing, it will take 7 hours to complete the job.

    b. This indicates that if you want to complete the job in 3 hours, you will need to have 6 people working on the job.

    c. $f^{-1}(x) = \dfrac{12}{x-1}$

4. **a.** $y = \dfrac{x-9}{4}$

    b. $y = \dfrac{7x+5}{2}$

LESSON 1 QUIZ

Form B

1. Suppose a message was first coded by assigning numbers to letters as shown below.

1	2	3	4	5	6	7	8	9	10	11	12	13	14
A	B	C	D	E	F	G	H	I	J	K	L	M	N

15	16	17	18	19	20	21	22	23	24	25	26	27
O	P	Q	R	S	T	U	V	W	X	Y	Z	

Brian then encrypted a message using the function $f(x) = 2x + 3$.

a. If the received message is given in encrypted form by 9, 5, 27, 27, 57, 29, 13, what was the message that was sent?

b. Explain in words how you could decode any message encrypted by the function $f(x) = 2x + 3$.

c. What function would decode any message encrypted by $f(x) = 2x + 3$?

b. Sydney wants to use a more complicated function for encrypting messages. She suggests using $g(x) = x^2 - 6x + 10$. What problems might arise if Sydney used this function? Be as specific as possible.

e. Suggest a different quadratic function that would be better for Sydney to use. Explain why your function does not have the same problems as Sydney's function does.

2. On the grid below, draw a graph of a function that does not have an inverse. Then explain why your function does not have an inverse.

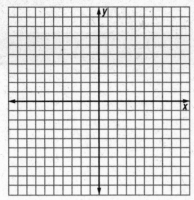

3. The height of a stack of pennies is a function of the number of pennies in the stack.

   a. Does this function have an inverse? Explain your reasoning.

   b. Explain what the inverse function will tell you about the variables in this situation.

4. Find an algebraic rule for the inverse of each function.

   a. $f(x) = \dfrac{5x - 6}{7}$

   b. $g(x) = \dfrac{4}{x + 1}$

LESSON 1 QUIZ

Form B
Suggested Solutions

1. **a.** CALL ME

   b. First, subtract 3 from the number and then divide that result by 2. Then use the chart above Part a to find the corresponding letter.

   c. $y = \frac{x-3}{2}$

   d. There are two different pairs of letters that would be encrypted as the same number: **A** and **E** would both be encrypted as **5** and **B** and **D** would both be encrypted as **2**. These letters would be difficult to decode. (Note that students only need to identify one of these pairs of letters.)

   e. Functions will vary. $y = x^2$ is one option. Any quadratic function that has a vertex with *x*-coordinate less than or equal to 1 or greater than or equal to 27 will encode each letter as a different number and will not have the same problem as Sydney's function.

2. Sketches will vary. Explanations should indicate two points on the graph with different *x*-coordinates but the same *y*-coordinate.

3. **a.** Yes, this function has an inverse; associated with each height is a unique number of pennies.

   b. The inverse function will tell you the number of pennies needed to produce a stack of a specified height.

4. **a.** $y = \frac{7x+6}{5}$

   b. $y = \frac{4}{x} - 1$

Think About This Situation

Solving equations like those in the three exponential growth and decay situations below is a kind of inverse problem. In each case, you know the output of a function but need to find the corresponding input.

a How could you estimate solutions for the given equations by exploring patterns in tables and graphs of function values?

b How would you approach solution of each equation by algebraic reasoning?

- If a count shows 50 bacteria in a lab dish at the start of an experiment and that number is predicted to double every hour, then to estimate the time when there will be 10,000 bacteria in the dish, you need to solve the equation $50(2^t) = 10,000$.

- The Washington Nationals baseball team was purchased in 2006 for 450 million dollars. To find how long it will take for the value of this investment to reach $1 billion, if it increases at the fairly conservative rate of 5% per year, you need to solve the equation $450(1.05^t) = 1,000$.

- If 500 mg of a medicine enters a hospital patient's bloodstream at noon and decays exponentially at a rate of 15% per hour, the amount remaining active in the patient's blood t hours later will be given by $d(t) = 500(0.85^t)$. To find the time when only 25 mg of the original amount remains active, you need to solve $25 = 500(0.85^t)$.

Summarize
the Mathematics

In this investigation, you reviewed the definition of the base 10 or common logarithm function. You then considered the ways that this function can be used to solve inverse problems involving exponential functions with base 10.

a How would you explain to someone who did not know about logarithms what the expression log $b = a$ tells about the numbers a and b?

b What can be said about the value of log y in each case below? Give brief justifications of your answers.

  i. $0 < y < 1$

  ii. $10 < y < 100$

  iii. $0.1 < y < 1$

  iv. $1 < y < 10$

  v. $100 < y < 1,000$

  vi. $0.01 < y < 0.1$

c Describe the main steps in solving equations in these forms for x.

  i. $10^{ax + b} = c$

  ii. $k(10^{ax + b}) = c$

Be prepared to explain your ideas to the class.

Summarize
the Mathematics

In this investigation, you learned how to use logarithms to solve equations related to exponential functions with any base, $b > 0$.

a How can any exponential function with rule in the form $f(x) = b^x$ $(b > 0)$ be written in an equivalent form using 10 as the base for the exponential expression?

b How can logarithms be used to solve any equation like $a(b^x) = c$ $(b > 0)$?

Be prepared to explain your ideas to the class.

Summarize the Mathematics

In this investigation, you learned properties of logarithms that can be used to write logarithmic and exponential expressions in useful equivalent forms.

a Why are the functions $f(x) = 10^x$ and $g(x) = \log x$ inverses of each other?

b Rewrite each of these expressions in an equivalent form.

 i. $\log (pn)$

 ii. $\log (p \div n)$

 iii. $\log (n^p)$

c Explain how properties of logarithms can be used to solve equations like $a(b^{kx}) = c$.

Be prepared to explain your ideas to the class.

LESSON 2 QUIZ

Form A

1. Without using your calculator, determine if each of the following statements is true or false. Explain your reasoning.

   a. $\log 10{,}000 = 4$

   b. $\log 0.01 = \frac{1}{2}$

   c. There is no value of x such that $10^x = -54$.

2. Without using your calculator, determine which of the following statements is true. Explain how you determined your answer without the use of your calculator.

   I. $900 < \log 925 < 1{,}000$

   II. $2 < \log 925 < 3$

   III. $3 < \log 925 < 4$

   IV. $9 < \log 925 < 10$

3. Consider the function $f(x) = 24^x$.

   a. Explain why the values of the function could be approximated using the rule $g(x) = 10^{1.38x}$.

   b. Solve the equation $24^x = 96$.

4. Recall that a sound with intensity 10^x watts/cm² has a decibel rating of $10x + 120$. The sound intensity of a popping balloon is 5,011 watts/cm². What is the decibel rating for a popping balloon?

5. The amount of light that is able to pass through the water in a lake depends on the clarity of the water. Suppose that in one lake, the function rule for light intensity (measured in lux) at a depth of d meters is $I(d) = 60,000(0.25^d)$.

   a. What is the light intensity at a depth of 1 meter?

   b. Use algebra and logarithms to determine the depth at which the light intensity will be 3,000 lux. Show your work.

6. Use the definition of logarithm and properties of logarithms to show why each of the following statements is true.

   a. $\log 20 = \log 4 + \log 5$

   b. $\log 50 = 2 - \log 2$

   c. $\log 16 = 4 \log 2$

LESSON 2 QUIZ

Form A
Suggested Solutions

1. **a.** True; $10^4 = 10,000$.

   b. False; $10^{\frac{1}{2}} \neq 0.01$.

   c. True; 10^x will always be positive.

2. Statement II is correct since 925 is between $10^2 = 100$ and $10^3 = 1,000$.

3. **a.** Since $10^{1.38} \approx 24$, $10^{1.38x} \approx 24^x$.

   b. $24^x = 96$ can be approximated by $10^{1.38x} = 96$.

   So, $\log 10^{1.38x} = \log 96$

   $$1.38x = \log 96$$
   $$x = \frac{\log 96}{1.38} \approx 1.436$$

4. Solving $10^x = 5,011$ tells us that $x = \log 5,011 \approx 3.7$. Thus, the decibel rating is $10(3.7) + 120 \approx 157$ decibels.

5. **a.** 15,000 lux

   b. $60,000(0.25^d) = 3,000$

   $$0.25^d = 0.05$$

   Since $\log 0.25 \approx -0.602$, the above equation can be approximated by

   $$10^{-0.602d} = 0.05$$
   $$-0.602d = \log 0.05$$
   $$d = \frac{\log 0.05}{-0.602} \approx 2.16$$

   Thus, at a depth of approximately 2.16 m, the light intensity will be 3,000 lux.

6. **a.** $\log 20 = \log (4 \cdot 5) = \log 4 + \log 5$, since $\log AB = \log A + \log B$.

   b. $\log 50 = \log \frac{100}{2} = \log 100 - \log 2 = 2 - \log 2$, since $\log \frac{A}{B} = \log A - \log B$ and $\log 100 = 2$.

   c. $\log 16 = \log 2^4 = 4 \log 2$, since $\log A^B = B \log A$.

LESSON 2 QUIZ

Form B

1. Without using your calculator, find the value of each of the following expressions. Explain your reasoning.

   a. log 1,000

   b. log 100^3

   c. $10^{\log k}$

   d. log 10^{a+b}

2. Atmospheric pressure decreases as the altitude above Earth increases. One formula that gives atmospheric pressure P (in grams per square centimeter) as a function of height above Earth h (in kilometers) is $P = 1{,}035\left(0.5^{\frac{h}{5.8}}\right)$.

   a. Jessica rewrote this function as $P = 1{,}035(0.8874^h)$. Explain what she did to find this equivalent function rule.

   b. Davonte wants to rewrite this formula so that it is in the form $P = 1{,}035(10^{kh})$. What is the correct value for k?

   c. Use algebraic reasoning with one of the equations above to determine the height at which the atmospheric pressure will be 600 grams per square centimeter. Show your work.

3. While working on a problem, Maria used her calculator to evaluate log 156.81. She got 1.1 as the result. Her partner looked at this value and knew immediately that it was not correct. Explain how her partner could know this without using a calculator.

4. In 2008, the population of Honduras was about 7.64 million people and it was growing at a rate of 2.02% per year. For this task, assume that the annual growth rate stays the same.

   a. Write a function rule for $P(t)$, the population in millions of Honduras t years after 2008.

   b. Based on this information, when is the population expected to reach 10 million people? Find an exact answer using logarithms and other algebraic reasoning.

5. If log 8 = a and log 5 = b, determine if each of the following statements is true or false. Explain your reasoning.

   a. $\log 2 = \frac{a}{3}$

   b. $\log 25 = b^2$

   c. $\log 40 = a + b$

   d. $\log \frac{1}{8} = \frac{1}{a}$

6. Solve each equation for x.

   a. $10^{3x-2} = 4{,}239$

   b. $2(1.4)^{x+1} = 926$

Form B
Suggested Solutions

1. a. $\log 1{,}000 = 3$ because $10^3 = 1{,}000$.

 b. $\log 100^3 = 6$ because $\log 100^3 = \log 10^6$.

 c. $10^{\log k} = k$ because $\log k$ is the power that you raise 10 to in order to get k.

 d. $\log 10^{a+b} = a + b$ because $10^{a+b} = 10^{a+b}$.

2. a. She evaluated $0.5^{\frac{1}{5.8}}$ to get 0.8874.

 b. $k = \log 0.8874 \approx -0.052$

 c. $1{,}035(10^{-0.052h}) = 600$

$$10^{-0.052h} = \frac{600}{1{,}035}$$

$$-0.052h = \log \frac{600}{1{,}035}$$

$$h = \frac{\log \frac{600}{1{,}035}}{-0.052} \approx 4.55 \text{ km}$$

3. Since 156.81 is between $100 = 10^2$ and $1{,}000 = 10^3$, the log of 156.81 must be between 2 and 3.

4. a. $P(t) = 7.65(1.0202^t)$

 b. $10 = 7.65(1.0202^t)$

$$t = \frac{\log \frac{10}{7.65}}{\log 1.0202} \approx 13.39 \text{ years after 2008}$$

5. a. True; $\log 8 = \log 2^3 = 3 \log 2 = a$, so $\log 2 = \frac{a}{3}$

 b. False; $\log 25 = \log 5^2 = 2 \log 5 = 2b \neq b^2$

 c. True; $\log 40 = \log (8 \cdot 5) = \log 8 + \log 5 = a + b$

 d. False; $\log \frac{1}{8} = -a$

6. a. $10^{3x-2} = 4{,}239$

$$3x - 2 = \log 4{,}239$$

$$x = \frac{\log 4{,}239 + 2}{3}$$

$$x \approx 1.88$$

 b. $2(1.4)^{x+1} = 926$

$$1.4^{x+1} = 463$$

$$x + 1 = \frac{\log 463}{\log 1.4}$$

$$x = \frac{\log 463}{\log 1.4} - 1$$

$$x \approx 17.24$$

Think About This **Situation**

Solving equations like those below that ask for times when tidal water has a specified depth is an inverse problem. You know the output of the function, and you need to find the corresponding input.

ⓐ What is the minimum depth of the water on the two particular days? The maximum depth?

ⓑ How could you estimate solutions for the given equations by exploring patterns in tables and graphs of function values?

ⓒ How would you approach solution of each equation by using algebraic reasoning and properties of the sine and cosine functions?

ⓓ What role could the **sin**⁻¹ or **cos**⁻¹ calculator commands have in solving these equations?

- On one particular day, the depth function is

$$d(t) = 11 + 3 \sin 0.5t.$$

To find the time(s) between noon and midnight when the depth of the water is 13 feet, you need to solve $11 + 3 \sin 0.5t = 13$.

- On a later date, the depth function is

$$d(t) = 11 - 3 \cos 0.5t.$$

To find the time(s) between noon and midnight when the depth of the water is 10 feet, you need to solve $11 - 3 \cos 0.5t = 10$.

Defining the Inverse Sine Function
Problem 1

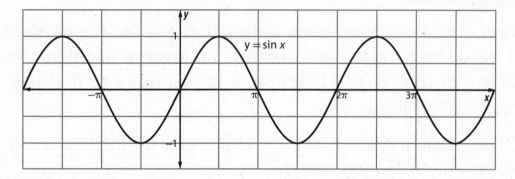

1. Find coordinates of points on the given graph that represent solutions for the following equations. Use what you know about the sine function to find exact values for the coordinates, where possible. Scan the given graph, a technology-generated table of $y = \sin x$, or a technology-produced graph of $y = \sin x$ to get good estimates of the coordinates as a check on your trigonometric reasoning.

   a. $\sin x = 0.5$ **b.** $\sin x = -1$

   c. $\sin x = 1$ **d.** $\sin x = -0.5$

The Sine and Inverse Sine Functions

Problem 4

4. Mathematical convention defines the **inverse sine** function as follows.

$$\sin^{-1} k = x \text{ if } \sin x = k \text{ and } -\frac{\pi}{2} \le x \le \frac{\pi}{2}$$

The inverse sine function is also called the *arcsine* function and written arcsin x.

a. Why do you think the definition focuses on the interval $-\frac{\pi}{2} \le x \le \frac{\pi}{2}$ to define values of the inverse sine function, rather than another interval of length π such as one of those you described in Part d of Problem 3?

b. What are the domain and the range of the inverse sine function?

c. The graph below shows the function $y = \sin x$ on a square window of $-1.57 \le x \le 1.57$ and $-1.57 \le y \le 1.57$. On this graph, sketch the graph of $y = \sin^{-1} x$. Check your sketch using technology that displays both functions on a square window.

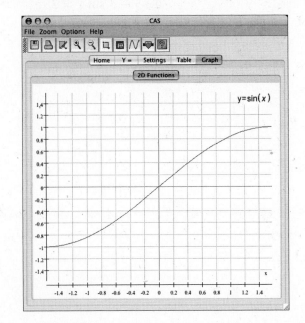

Name _____

Date _____

Inverse Sine of Degrees and Radians
Problems 11 and 12

11. In previous units, you learned the values of the sine function for some special angles. Use what you know about the sine of special angles and the inverse sine function to complete the following table. Use radian measures between $-\frac{\pi}{2}$ and $\frac{\pi}{2}$ and degree measures between $-90°$ and $90°$.

u	-1	$-\frac{\sqrt{3}}{2}$		$-\frac{1}{2}$	0	$\frac{1}{2}$			1
$\sin^{-1} u$ (in radians)			$-\frac{\pi}{4}$			$\frac{\pi}{6}$		$\frac{\pi}{3}$	
$\sin^{-1} u$ (in degrees)	-90					30	45		

12. Use algebra and trigonometry to find all solutions of the following equations in both degrees and radians. Give exact solutions, if possible.

   a. $2 \sin x = -\sqrt{3}$

   b. $2 \sin x - 3 = 1$

   c. $3 \sin x + 2 = 4$

   d. $5 - 3 \sin x = 2$

Student Master • *use with pages 582 and 583*

Summarize the Mathematics

In this investigation, you learned about the inverse sine function and some of its properties. You also used the inverse sine function to solve linear equations involving the sine.

ⓐ The sine function defined over the set of real numbers has no inverse function. Why not?

ⓑ Explain how the inverse sine function was defined in this lesson in order to overcome the difficulties you noted in Part a.

ⓒ Describe the conditions under which $\sin^{-1}(\sin x) = x$. Explain your reasoning.

ⓓ Consider an equation of the form $a \sin x + b = c$ which is linear in $\sin x$.

   i. How is solving this equation similar to and different from solving $ax + b = c$ which is linear in x?

   ii. Under what conditions on a, b, and c does $a \sin x + b = c$ have solutions?

   iii. If you know one solution, how many solutions will there be? Describe how to find all solutions.

Be prepared to share your thinking and procedures with the class.

Summarize
the Mathematics

In this investigation, you learned about the inverse cosine and inverse tangent functions, and you used those functions to help solve linear equations involving the cosine or tangent.

ⓐ What are the domain and range of $y = \cos^{-1} x$?

ⓑ Sketch the graph of $y = \cos^{-1} x$.

ⓒ Describe a strategy that uses the inverse cosine function to solve equations in the form $a \cos x + b = c$.

ⓓ What are the domain and range of $y = \tan^{-1} x$?

ⓔ Sketch the graph of $y = \tan^{-1} x$.

ⓕ Describe a strategy that uses the inverse tangent function to solve equations in the form $a \tan x + b = c$.

Be prepared to share your thinking and procedures with the class.

LESSON 3 QUIZ

Form A

1. Maya knows that $\sin \frac{5\pi}{6} = \frac{1}{2}$. Explain how she can use this fact to determine $\sin^{-1}\left(\frac{1}{2}\right)$.

2. Give a value of x in degrees for which $\cos^{-1}(\cos x) \neq x$. Explain your reasoning.

3. If possible, find a single solution to each equation. Give answers in exact radians.

   a. $\cos x = \frac{\sqrt{3}}{2}$

   b. $\tan x = -1$

   c. $3 \sin x = 5$

   d. $4 \cos 2x + 3 = 3$

4. Find all possible solutions to each equation. Give answers in exact radians where possible and to the nearest tenth of a radian otherwise.

   a. $\sin x = -0.7$

   b. $8 \cos x + 1 = 2$

5. On a particular day, the depth of water in feet at the entrance to a harbor is modeled by the function $d(t) = 6 + 4 \sin 0.5t$, where t is hours after 9 A.M.

   a. What are the minimum and maximum depths on this day? When do they first occur after 9:00 A.M.? Show algebraic reasoning that can be used to find the answers.

   Minimum Depth: *Time it occurs:*

   Maximum Depth: *Time it occurs:*

   b. Edgar has a boat that needs at least 4 feet of water. During what times after 9:00 A.M. and before 10:00 P.M. will the water at the entrance to the harbor be less than 4 feet deep? Write and solve an equation to help you answer this question.

LESSON 3 QUIZ

Form A
Suggested Solutions

1. Since the range of $f(x) = \sin^{-1} x$ is $-\frac{\pi}{2} < x < \frac{\pi}{2}$, she needs to determine the angle measure θ in this range that has $\sin \theta = \frac{1}{2}$. This will be $\frac{5\pi}{6} - \frac{\pi}{2} = \frac{\pi}{6}$. So, $\sin^{-1}\left(\frac{1}{2}\right) = \frac{\pi}{6}$.

2. Since the range of $f(x) = \cos^{-1} x$ is $0° < x < 180°$, any value of x not in the interval $[0°, 180°]$ will make $\cos^{-1}(\cos x) \neq x$.

3. **a.** $x = \frac{\pi}{6}$ **b.** $x = \frac{3\pi}{4}$

    c. No solution   **d.** $\cos 2x = 0$
$$2x = \frac{\pi}{2}$$
$$x = \frac{\pi}{4}$$

4. **a.** $x = -0.775 + 2\pi n$ for any integer n

    or

    $x = 3.917 + 2\pi n$ for any integer n

    b. $\cos x = \frac{1}{8}$

    $x = 1.445 + 2\pi n$ for any integer n

    $x = 2\pi - 1.445 + 2\pi n$

    $= 4.838 + 2\pi n$ for any integer n

5. **a.** The minimum depth will be 2 feet. It will occur when $\sin 0.5t = -1$. This happens when $0.5t = \frac{3\pi}{2}$, or $t = 3\pi \approx 9.42$ hours.

    Minimum Depth: 2 ft   *Time it occurs:* approximately 9:25 P.M.

    The maximum depth will be 10 feet and will occur when $\sin 0.5t = 1$. This happens when $0.5t = \frac{\pi}{2}$, or $t = \pi$. So, the maximum depth first occurs 3.14 hours after 9 A.M.

    Maximum Depth: 10 ft   *Time it occurs:* approximately 12:08 P.M.

    b. $6 + 4 \sin 0.5t = 4$
$$\sin 0.5t = -\frac{1}{2}$$
$$0.5t = \frac{7\pi}{6}$$
$$t \approx 7.33$$

    or
$$0.5t = \frac{11\pi}{6}$$
$$t \approx 11.52$$

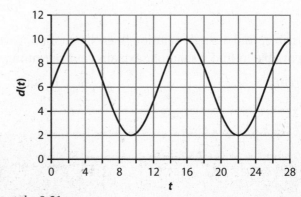

    So, the water in the harbor will be less than 4 feet deep from approximately 4:20 P.M. until approximately 8:31 P.M.

Name _____

Date _____

LESSON 3 QUIZ

Form B

1. Give the domain and range of each of the following functions.

   a. $s(x) = \sin^{-1} x$

   Domain: _____ Range: _____

   b. $c(x) = \cos^{-1} x$

   Domain: _____ Range: _____

   c. $t(x) = \tan^{-1} x$

   Domain: _____ Range: _____

2. The solution to an equation like $\cos x = k$ is related to the solution of $\cos^{-1} k = x$.

   a. How many solutions are there to $\cos x = k$ for $-1 \le k \le 1$? Explain.

   b. How many solutions are there to the equation $\cos^{-1} k = x$ for $-1 \le k \le 1$? Explain.

   c. Explain how you can use the solution to $\cos^{-1} k = x$ to find all the solutions to $\cos x = k$ for $-1 \le k \le 1$.

3. If possible, find a single solution to each equation. Give your answer in exact radians. If it is not possible to find a solution, explain your reasoning.

   a. $2 \sin x = -\sqrt{3}$ **b.** $\tan x = \sqrt{3}$

   c. $4 \cos x + 1 = 3$ **d.** $3 \sin x + 1 = -5$

4. Find all solutions of each equation.

   a. $3 \cos x = -2.31$ **b.** $5 \sin x + 4 = 6$

5. Consider $\triangle ABC$ with $AB = 7$, $AC = 12$, and $m\angle C = 30°$. Use the Law of Sines to find all possible values for $m\angle B$. Show your work. $\left(\text{Recall that the Law of Sines indicates that in any } \triangle ABC, \dfrac{a}{\sin A} = \dfrac{b}{\sin B} = \dfrac{c}{\sin C}.\right)$

LESSON 3 QUIZ

Form B
Suggested Solutions

1. **a.** *Domain:* $-1 \le x \le 1$ *Range:* $-\frac{\pi}{2} \le s(x) \le \frac{\pi}{2}$

   b. *Domain:* $-1 \le x \le 1$ *Range:* $0 \le c(x) \le \pi$

   c. *Domain:* All real numbers   *Range:* $-\frac{\pi}{2} < t(x) < \frac{\pi}{2}$

2. **a.** Because $y = \cos x$ is a periodic function with range from -1 to 1 inclusive, there is an infinite number of solutions to $\cos x = k$ for $-1 \le k \le 1$.

   b. There is only one solution to $\cos^{-1} k = x$ for $-1 \le k \le 1$ because x must be between 0 and π inclusive.

   c. Say that the primary solution to $\cos^{-1} k = x$ is $x = \theta$. Then another solution will be $x = -\theta$. But you must also add $2\pi n$ to each of these. So, the solutions will be $\theta + 2\pi n$ and $-\theta + 2\pi n$ for any integer n.

3. **a.** $x = -\frac{\pi}{3}$ **b.** $x = \frac{\pi}{4}$

   c. $x = \frac{\pi}{3}$ **d.** No solution

4. **a.** $x = \cos^{-1}\left(\frac{-2.31}{3}\right) = -2.31$

   $x \approx 2.45 + 2\pi n$ for any integer n

   $x \approx -2.45 + 2\pi n$ for any integer n

   b. $x = \sin^{-1}\left(\frac{2}{5}\right) \approx 0.41$

   or

   $x = \pi - 0.41 \approx 2.73$

   $x \approx 0.41 + 2\pi n$ for any integer n

   $x \approx 2.73 + 2\pi n$ for any integer n

5.

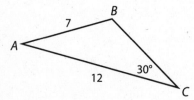

$$\frac{7}{\sin 30^\circ} = \frac{12}{\sin B}$$

$$\sin B = \frac{12 \sin 30^\circ}{\sin B}$$

$$B = \sin^{-1}\left(\frac{6}{7}\right)$$

$$B = 59^\circ \text{ or } B = 180^\circ - 59^\circ = 121^\circ$$

Summarize the Mathematics

In this unit, you explored inverses of functions with particular attention to inverses of exponential functions and of trigonometric functions.

a What does it mean to say that two functions f and g are inverses of each other?

b How can you determine whether a function $f(x)$ has an inverse by studying:

   i. a table of $(x, f(x))$ values?

   ii. a graph of the function?

   iii. a definition in words or a symbolic rule for the function?

c Among the families of functions that you have studied most closely and used most often:

   i. which almost always have inverses?

   ii. which do not generally have inverses?

d How can the statement "$\log_{10} a = b$" be expressed in equivalent form using exponents?

e How can properties of logarithms be used to write these algebraic expressions in equivalent form?

   i. $\log mn = \ldots$

   ii. $\log m^n = \ldots$

   iii. $\log \frac{m}{n} = \ldots$

Summarize
the Mathematics
Cont.

f How can properties of logarithms be used to solve exponential functions like $a(b^x) = c$?

g What does it mean to say that $\sin^{-1} x = k$?

h What are the domain and range of $\sin^{-1} x$? Of $\cos^{-1} x$? Of $\tan^{-1} x$?

i How can inverse trigonometric functions be used to solve trigonometric equations?

Be prepared to share your examples and descriptions with the class.

Name _____

Date _____

UNIT SUMMARY

In this unit, you developed skill in recognizing and finding rules for inverses of functions and using those inverses to solve a variety of decoding problems. You also learned how to use logarithms to solve exponential equations and inverse trigonometric functions to solve trigonometric equations.

Describe conditions required for a function to have an inverse.

_____

_____

Explain how relationships between functions and their inverses are shown in:

- Tables of values for each function _____

_____

_____

- Graphs of each function _____

_____

_____

Show the algebraic reasoning that leads to rules for inverses of functions with rules in the form:

- $f(x) = mx + b$ • $g(x) = \dfrac{m}{x}$

Describe the relationship between common logarithms and base 10 exponential expressions.

Describe a strategy for using logarithms to solve equations in the form $10^{mx + b} = c$.

Describe a strategy for using logarithms to solve equations in the form $a^x = c$.

How can each of these expressions be written in useful equivalent forms?

- $\log ab =$

- $\log (a \div b) =$

- $\log a^n =$

- $\log \left(\frac{1}{a}\right) =$

Explain in words the ways that values of $\sin^{-1} x$, $\cos^{-1} x$, and $\tan^{-1} x$ are determined.

_____

_____

_____

How could you use inverse trig functions to solve equations?

- $a \sin x + b = c$

- $a \cos x + b = c$

- $a \tan x + b = c$

Name _____

Date _____

UNIT TEST

Form A

1. Suppose that the cost (in dollars) for mailing a package weighing x pounds is given by the function $f(x) = 14.95 + 3x$.

   a. Find $f(5)$. Explain what it tells you about the variables in this situation.

   b. Find $f^{-1}(38.95)$. Explain what it tells you about the variables in this situation.

   c. Write an algebraic rule for $f^{-1}(x)$.

2. Below is a table of values for $f(x)$ and $g(x)$. Based on the information in the tables, could $g(x)$ be the inverse function for $f(x)$? Explain your reasoning.

x	−6	−5	−3	0	1	3	6
$f(x)$	6	3	1	0	−3	−5	−6
$g(x)$	−5	−3	0	1	3	6	7

3. Write an algebraic rule for the inverse of each function.

   a. $f(x) = \dfrac{4}{x}$

   b. $h(x) = \log x$

   c. $s(x) = \sin x$

4. In this unit, you explored the relationship between decibels and sound intensity. There is also a relationship between decibels and the pressure sounds exert on the human ear. This pressure is measured in Newtons per square meter (N/m^2). The table below displays this relationship for several decibel levels.

Pressure on Ear (in N/m²)	Decibel Level (in dB)
0.002	40
0.02	60
0.2	80
2	100
20	120

One form of the rule for the relationship between pressure on the ear P and decibel level D is $D = 10 \log \left(\dfrac{P}{2 \times 10^{-5}} \right)^2$.

a. If a sound exerts a pressure of 2,000 N/m^2, what is the decibel level for the sound? Show your work or explain your reasoning.

b. The threshold of hearing, that is, the faintest sound that can be consistently heard, has a decibel level of 0 dB. What amount of pressure does such a sound place on the ear? Show your work or explain your reasoning.

c. Another form of the rule for the relationship between decibel level and pressure exerted on the ear is $D = 20 \log P + 94$. Use properties of logarithms and the ability of your calculator to evaluate the log of any number to show that this rule and the rule given earlier in this task are equivalent.

5. Without using your calculator, determine if each statement is true or false. Explain your reasoning.

   a. $3 < \log 431.7 < 4$

   b. $\log(-10) = -1$

   c. $\sin^{-1}(\sin 300°) = 300°$

6. Use symbolic reasoning and properties of logarithms to solve each equation.

   a. $\log 10^8 = x$

   b. $426 = 3(2.1^x)$

   c. $9.3^{2x+1} = 930$

7. Find all solutions to each equation. Give answers in radians. Give exact answers whenever possible.

   a. $\tan x = -0.5$

   b. $6 \sin x = 3$

   c. $\cos x - 5 = -5.8$

UNIT TEST

Form A
Suggested Solutions

1. **a.** $f(5) = 29.95$. This indicates that a package weighing 5 pounds will cost $29.95 to mail.

    b. $f^{-1}(38.95) = 8$. This tells us that if the shipping cost is $38.95, then the package weighs 8 pounds.

    c. $f^{-1}(x) = \frac{x - 14.95}{3}$

2. Since $f(-5) = 3$, we know that $f^{-1}(3) = 5$. But $g(3) = 6$, so $g(x)$ is not the inverse of $f(x)$. (Students may choose to use any $(x, f(x))$ pair in their explanations.)

3. **a.** $f^{-1}(x) = \frac{4}{x}$

    b. $g^{-1}(x) = 10^x$

    c. $s^{-1}(x) = \sin^{-1} x$

4. **a.** $D = 10 \log \left(\frac{2 \times 10^3}{2 \times 10^{-5}}\right)^2 = 10 \log (10^8)^2 = 10 \log 10^{16} = 160$ dB

    b. In order for the decibel level to be 0, the expression inside of the parentheses must be 1. (Since $\log 1 = 0$.) So if a sound has a decibel level of 0, the pressure exerted on the ear must be 2×10^{-5} N/m^2.

    c. $D = 10 \log \left(\frac{P}{2 \times 10^{-5}}\right)^2 = 20 \log \frac{P}{2 \times 10^{-5}}$

    $$= 20(\log P - \log (2 \times 10^{-5}))$$

    $$= 20(\log P - (-4.7))$$

    $$= 20 \log P + 94$$

5. **a.** False; $2 < \log 431.7 < 3$ since $10^2 = 100 < 431.7 < 1{,}000 = 10^3$.

    b. False; $\log (-10)$ is undefined since 10 to any power is a positive number.

    c. False; the range of $y = \sin^{-1} x$ is $90° \le y \le 90°$, so $\sin^{-1} (\sin 300°) = -60°$.

6. a. $x = 8$

   b. $3(2.1^x) = 426$

   $2.1^x = 142$

   $x = \dfrac{\log 142}{\log 2.1} \approx 6.68$

   c. $2x + 1 = \dfrac{\log 930}{\log 9.3} \approx 3.065$

   $2x \approx 2.065$

   $x \approx 1.033$

7. a. $\tan^{-1} 0.5 \approx -0.46$

   The solutions are approximately $-0.46 + \pi n$ for any integer n.

   b. $\sin^{-1}\left(\dfrac{1}{2}\right) = \dfrac{\pi}{6}$

   The solutions are approximately $\dfrac{\pi}{6} + 2\pi n$ and $\dfrac{5\pi}{6} + 2\pi n$ for any integer n.

   c. $\cos^{-1}(-0.8) \approx 2.5$

   The solutions are approximately $2.5 + 2\pi n$ and $3.78 + 2\pi n$ for any integer n.

UNIT TEST

Form B

1. For each function below, determine if an inverse function exists over the entire domain. If it does not, identify how the domain could be restricted so that the function will have an inverse.

   a.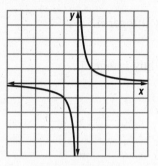

   b.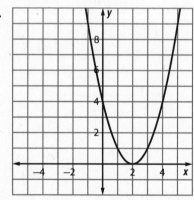

   c. $f(x) = \sin x$

2. Write an algebraic rule for the inverse of each function.

   a. $f(x) = x^3$

   b. $g(x) = 10^x$

   c. $h(x) = \dfrac{6}{x + 3}$

3. Atmospheric pressure under water P (in pounds per square inch) is a function of water depth d (in feet) and can be determined using $P(d) = 14.7 + 0.445d$.

   a. Find $P(54)$. Explain what it tells you about the variables in this situation.

   b. At what depth is the atmospheric pressure 26.27 pounds per square inch?

   c. Find the value of $P^{-1}(31.7)$.

   d. Find a rule for $P^{-1}(x)$.

4. For children not growing at a normal rate, physicians sometimes prescribe a growth hormone that deteriorates at a rate of 81% per hour. If the dosage is 10 mg, then the amount A (in mg) of the hormone remaining in the body after t hours is given by $A = 10(0.19^t)$.

   a. How much of the hormone is still in the child's body after two hours?

   b. Use symbolic reasoning to determine when the amount of hormone left in the child's body will be 5 mg. Show your work.

   c. Seth wanted to write a rule that gave the elapsed time as a function of the amount of growth hormone remaining in the body. So, he solved $A = 10(0.19^t)$ for t. Seth's rule was $t = \dfrac{-1 + \log A}{\log 0.19}$. Is his rule correct? Explain your reasoning or show your work.

5. Suppose that $\log A = 5$ and $\log B = 2$. Determine the value of each of the following.

   a. $\log A^2$

   b. $\log \frac{A}{B}$

   c. $\log AB^3$

   d. $\log \frac{1}{A}$

6. Use symbolic reasoning and properties of logarithms to solve each equation.

   a. $\log 10{,}000 = 2x$

   b. $10^{x+1} + 87 = 1{,}503$

   c. $4(3^x) = 127$

7. Find all solutions to each equation. Give exact answers whenever possible.

   a. $\cos x = 0.2$

   b. $-2 \sin x = \sqrt{3}$

   c. $\tan x + 3 = 2$

8. If $0° \le x \le 360°$, find all possible values of x if $\sin (x + 20°) = 0.5$.

UNIT TEST

Form B
Suggested Solutions

1. **a.** The function has an inverse over the entire domain.

   b. The function does not have an inverse over the entire domain. Restricting the domain to $x \geq 2$ (or $x \leq 2$) will make the inverse a function.

   c. The domain of the function must be restricted. The standard restriction is $-\frac{\pi}{2} < x < \frac{\pi}{2}$, but others are possible.

2. **a.** $f^{-1}(x) = x^{\frac{1}{3}}$

   b. $g^{-1}(x) = \log x$

   c. $h^{-1}(x) = \frac{6 - 3x}{x}$

3. **a.** $P(54) = 14.7 + 0.445(54) = 38.73$. This indicates that at a depth of 54 feet, the pressure is 38.73 pounds per square inch.

   b. $26.27 = 14.7 + 0.445d$
   $d = 26$ feet

   c. $P^{-1}(31.7) \approx 38.2$

   d. $P^{-1}(x) = \frac{x - 14.7}{0.445}$

4. **a.** $10(0.19^2) \approx 0.361$ mg

   b. $10(0.19^t) = 5$
   $0.19^t = 0.5$
   $t \log 0.19 = \log 0.5$
   $t = \frac{\log 0.5}{\log 0.19} \approx 0.417$ hours, or about 25 minutes

   c. The rule is correct.
   $10(0.19^t) = A$
   $0.19^t = \frac{A}{10}$
   $t \log 0.19 = \log \frac{A}{10}$
   $t = \frac{\log \frac{A}{10}}{\log 0.19} = \frac{\log A - \log 10}{\log 0.19} = \frac{-1 + \log A}{\log 0.19}$

5. a. $\log A^2 = 2 \log A = 10$

   c. $\log AB^3 = \log A + 3 \log B = 3$

b. $\log \frac{A}{B} = \log A - \log B = -5$

d. $\log \frac{1}{A} = \log (A^{-1}) = -1 \log A = -5$

6. a. $4 = 2x$
   $2 = x$

   b. $10^{x+1} = 1{,}416$
   $x + 1 = \log 1{,}416$
   $x = \log 1{,}416 - 1 \approx 2.151$

   c. $4(3^x) = 127$
   $3^x = 31.75$
   $x = \dfrac{\log 31.75}{\log 3} \approx 3.15$

7. a. $x = 1.37 + 2\pi n$ for any integer n

   $x = -1.37 + 2\pi n$ for any integer n

   c. $x = -\dfrac{\pi}{4} + \pi n$ for any integer n

b. $x = -\dfrac{\pi}{3} + 2\pi n$ for any integer n

   $x = \dfrac{4\pi}{3} + 2\pi n$ for any integer n

8. $x + 20° = 30°$ or $x + 20° = 150°$
   $\quad\quad x = 10°$ or $\quad\quad\quad\quad x = 130°$

TAKE-HOME ASSESSMENTS

1. **a.** Some people consider activities such as bungee jumping or sky diving to be quite dangerous or risky. Other activities such as driving a car seem less likely to result in injury or death. One way to identify the likelihood of an event is to consider the probability of occurrence. The following are annual risks for Americans given as probabilities.

You will be injured if you play basketball regularly:	1 in 40
You will die of cancer:	1 in 500
You will be killed by a tornado:	1 in 2,000,000
You will contract the plague:	1 in 25,000,000
You will die of rabies:	1 in 100,000,000

Source: The Book of Risks, Lauden, Larry ©1995. Reprinted by John Wiley & Sons, Inc.

Design a method that uses a logarithmic scale to assign "risk numbers" that convey the significance of each of the above risks. Assign your "risk numbers" so that they indicate a low risk number for an event that is not likely to occur. Explain the reasons behind your method.

   b. Research how others have devised methods to assign risk factors. One possible source is the book *Up to Your Armpits in Alligators? How to Sort Out What Risks Are Worth Worrying About* by John Paling, 2nd edition. Information about the risk scale devised by the Palings can also be found in the brief article "Why Worry?" by Gary Stix in *Scientific American,* May 1995, pp. 20-21. Write a summary of your findings.

2. Cecilia deposited $400 into a savings account that will pay 5% interest compounded annually. At the same time, Aaron deposited $600 into a savings account that will pay 3% compounded annually. Assume that Cecilia and Aaron do not deposit any money into their accounts or take any money out of their accounts.

   a. Use graphs to determine when the two accounts will have the same amount of money. Show or explain your work.

   b. Use a spreadsheet to determine when the two accounts will have the same amount of money. Show or explain your work.

   c. Use algebraic reasoning to determine when the two accounts will have the same amount of money. Show or explain your work.

   d. Which of the above methods do you prefer? Explain your reasoning.

   e. Solve the general equation $ab^x = cd^x$ for x. Show your work and justify your reasoning. Write your answer in what you consider to be simplest form. Explain why you think the form you give is the simplest form to use.

   f. Use your solution in Part e to determine when Cecilia's and Aaron's accounts will have the same balance. Show or explain your work.

3. Consider the equation $\sin x = k$ for $0 \leq x \leq 2\pi$.

    a. Determine a value for k such that the equation has the indicated number of solutions.

        i. Exactly one solution

        ii. Exactly two solutions

        iii. Exactly three solutions

        iv. No solutions

    b. Suppose that x is not restricted to the interval $[0, 2\pi]$. Find all solutions to the equation $\sin x = k$ for each of the values of k that you indicated in Part a.

TAKE-HOME ASSESSMENTS

Suggested Solutions

1. a. One example follows. Take the log of the values 40, 500, 2,000,000, and so on. Then take the reciprocal of those values and multiply by 10. This gives the risk numbers in the table below.

1 in	Risk Number
40	6.242
500	3.7051
2,000,000	1.587
25,000,000	1.357
100,000,000	1.25

This method assigns a proportionally much greater number to the events that are more likely to occur. In this way, the scale might help people more easily identify those things that are more dangerous. With this method, one might choose to classify an event with a risk number over $3\frac{1}{3}$ as a high risk since that risk number occurs when probability of the event is at least 1 in 1,000.

b. John and Sean Paling's logarithmic method takes the log of the probability and increases that result by 6. A sample table is provided below.

Probability of an Event Occurring	Risk Number
$\frac{1}{10}$	+5
$\frac{1}{100}$	+4
$\frac{1}{1,000}$	+3
$\frac{1}{10,000}$	+2
$\frac{1}{100,000}$	+1
$\frac{1}{1,000,000}$	0
$\frac{1}{10,000,000}$	−1
$\frac{1}{100,000,000}$	−2
$\frac{1}{1,000,000,000}$	−3
$\frac{1}{10,000,000,000}$	−4
$\frac{1}{100,000,000,000}$	−5

2. a. Function rules for balances in the two accounts are:

Cecilia: $C(x) = 400(1.05^x)$

Aaron: $A(x) = 600(1.03^x)$

Students should use technology to determine that the graphs of the functions intersect at approximately (21.08, 1,118.94). So, the two accounts will have approximately the same amount after 21.08 years.

b. Students should set up a spreadsheet to determine when the two accounts will have the same balance. They will not be able to find the exact time but will be able to see that after 21 years, the account balances are very close to each other. Cecilia's account will have a balance of $1,114.39, and Aaron's account balance will be $1,116.18.

c. $400(1.05^x) = 600(1.03^x)$

$$\frac{1.05^x}{1.03^x} = \frac{600}{400}$$

$$\left(\frac{1.05}{1.03}\right)^x = \frac{3}{2}$$

$$x = \frac{\log \frac{3}{2}}{\log \frac{1.05}{1.03}} \approx 21.08 \text{ years}$$

d. Student preferences will vary.

e. Students should supply reasoning for each of their steps in solving this equation for x. If students are having difficulty, you may want to suggest that they look back at their work in Part c. One simplified form is $x = \dfrac{\log \frac{c}{a}}{\log \frac{b}{d}} = \dfrac{\log c - \log a}{\log b - \log d}$.

f. $x = \dfrac{\log 600 - \log 400}{\log 1.05 - \log 1.03} \approx \dfrac{0.176091}{0.008352} \approx 21.08 \text{ years}$

3. a. Students' values of k will vary for parts i, ii, and iv.

   i. $k = 1$ or $k = -1$

   ii. $0 < k < 1$ or $-1 < k < 0$

   iii. $k = 0$

   iv. $k > 1$ or $k < -1$

b.   **i.** If $k = 1$, then $x = 2\pi n + \frac{\pi}{2}$ for any integer n.

      If $k = -1$, then $x = 2\pi n + \frac{3\pi}{2}$ for any integer n.

   ii. Solutions will depend on the values of k identified in Part a.

   iii. $x = \pi n$ for any integer n

PROJECT

Inverse Functions and Rates of Change

Purpose

In your study of functions, you have often investigated and described the rate of change of a function. In this unit, you learned about the inverse of a function. Specifically, you thought about when an inverse exists. In cases where one exists, you learned how to find a rule for it. In this project, you will look for relationships between the rate of change of a function and the rate of change of its inverse.

Directions

1. Consider the general rule for a linear function, $f(x) = mx + b$.

    a. Determine a general rule for $f^{-1}(x)$.

    b. Describe or sketch graphs of $f(x)$ and $f^{-1}(x)$.

    c. Describe the rate of change of $f(x)$ and $f^{-1}(x)$. Describe any relationships that you find between the rates of change of the function and its inverse.

2. Choose two different values of n with $n > 1$. For each one, complete Parts a–c of Item 1 for the power function $f(x) = x^n$, $x \geq 0$.

3. Choose two different whole number values for n. For each one, complete Parts a–c of Item 1 for the inverse variation function $f(x) = \frac{1}{x^n}$, $x \geq 0$.

4. Complete Parts a–c of Item 1 for the function $f(x) = 10^x$.

5. Complete Parts a–c of Item 1 for the function $f(x) = \cos x$, $0 \leq x < \pi$.

6. Write a report that contains all of your work on this project. Your report should be well-organized and carefully written, and your conclusions should be fully supported with specific details and logical reasoning.

Suggested Solutions
Inverse Functions and Rates of Change

This project asks students to explore the relationship between the rate of change of a function and the rate of change of its inverse. As they explore the relationship, students will review properties of linear, power, inverse variation, exponential, logarithmic, and trigonometric functions. Encourage students to think visually as they work on this project.

Suggested Timeline

This project is best completed by pairs or small groups of students working together. They can divide the work for Items 1–5 and then compare and contrast their results. You may want to look at students' work on Items 1–5 before students begin trying to write an answer to Item 6. If their work on Items 1–5 is not correct, they will have difficulty making any generalizations.

Solutions

1. **a.** $f^{-1}(x) = \dfrac{x - b}{m} = \dfrac{1}{m}x - \dfrac{b}{m}$

    b. Both of the graphs will be lines. The intercepts of $f(x)$ and $f^{-1}(x)$ will be b and $-\dfrac{b}{m}$ and the slopes will be m and $\dfrac{1}{m}$, respectively.

    c. The rate of change of $f(x)$ is constant and is m. The rate of change of $f^{-1}(x)$ is constant and is $\dfrac{1}{m}$. The rate of change of $f^{-1}(x)$ is the multiplicative inverse of the rate of change of $f(x)$.

2. Student work will depend on the values of n chosen. However, the overall patterns do not depend on the value of n. The solutions below are for $n = 2$.

    a. $f^{-1}(x) = x^{\frac{1}{2}}$

    c. The rate of change of $f(x)$ is always positive, and it is increasing at an increasing rate. The rate of change of $f^{-1}(x)$ is always positive, and it is increasing at a decreasing rate. For values close to zero, the rate of change of $f^{-1}(x)$ is greater than the rate of change of $f(x)$. For all other values, the rate of change of $f(x)$ is greater than the rate of change of $f^{-1}(x)$.

    b.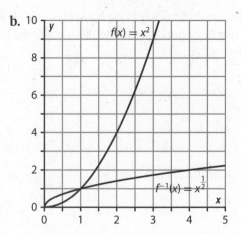

3. Student work will depend on the values of n chosen. However, the overall patterns do not depend on the value of n. The solutions below are for $n = 2$.

a. $f^{-1}(x) = \dfrac{1}{\sqrt{x}}$

b.

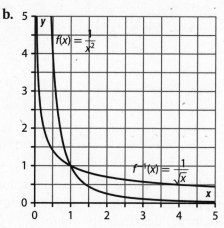

c. The rate of change of both $f(x)$ and $f^{-1}(x)$ is decreasing. $f^{-1}(x)$ decreases more rapidly between 0 and 1 than does $f(x)$. The rate of change of $f(x)$ is always greater than the rate of change of $f^{-1}(x)$. However, for $x > 1$, $f^{-1}(x)$ decreases more slowly than does $f(x)$.

4. a. $f^{-1}(x) = \dfrac{1}{\sqrt{x}}$

b. It is difficult to draw these on the same graph. You may want to encourage students to use different graphs. However, this makes it more difficult to compare the rates of change.

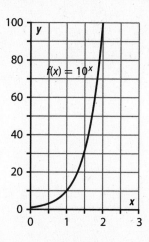 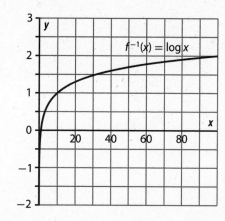

c. The rate of change of $f(x)$ is always positive, and it is increasing at an increasing rate. The rate of change of $f^{-1}(x)$ is always positive. But $f^{-1}(x)$ is increasing at a decreasing rate. For positive values very close to zero, the rate of change of $f^{-1}(x)$ is greater than that of $f(x)$. For all other possible values of x, the rate of change of $f(x)$ is greater than the rate of change of $f^{-1}(x)$.

5. a. $f^{-1}(x) = \cos^{-1}x$

b.

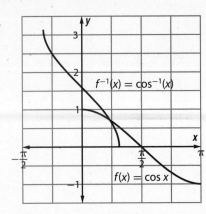

c. The rate of change of $f(x) = \cos x$ in the indicated domain is always negative. The function values decrease slowly when x is close to zero, more rapidly in the middle of the interval, and then more slowly as x approaches π. The rate of change of $f^{-1}(x)$ is also always negative. The values of $f^{-1}(x)$ change more rapidly than do the values of $f(x)$. The values of $f^{-1}(x)$ change most quickly when x is close to 1 or -1 and more slowly in the middle of the interval $[-1, 1]$.

6. Each group should complete a report of the work that it has done. You may need to help students with their organization of this work.

PROJECT

Solving Equations

Purpose

Algebraic equations come in many forms. During the last three years, you have learned a variety of techniques that you can use to find approximate and exact solutions to equations. Your techniques include using graphs, tables of values, and symbolic manipulation. Some of the equations that you solved had no solution, others had a finite number of solutions, and still others had an infinite number of solutions. As you work on this project, you will review and organize the different methods that you have learned for solving equations. You will also look for similarities among the different methods.

Directions

For this project, you will prepare a report that summarizes all that you know about solving equations. The purpose of your report is to convey to a mathematics teacher your knowledge about solving equations. Your report should address all of the questions and topics listed below. Organize your report in a way that you think best conveys your knowledge. When you are thinking about your answers to the questions below, be sure to consider linear, quadratic, direct and inverse power, exponential, polynomial, rational, logarithmic, and trigonometric equations.

Topics that your report should address:

Topic 1: Using tables and graphs to approximate solutions to equations

- For what types of equations can you approximate solutions using tables of values or graphs?
- How do you use tables of values to approximate solutions to equations?
- How do you use graphs to approximate solutions to equations?
- Why are the solutions that you get often only approximations and not exact solutions?
- When can you get exact solutions to an equation using tables or graphs?
- How can you determine if the solution that you get is an approximation or the exact solution to the equation?

Topic 2: Symbolic reasoning methods for solving equations

- What symbolic reasoning methods do you know for solving equations?
- For what types of equations do the different methods work?
- How do you use each method to solve an equation?
- How are different methods related to each other?

Topic 3: Number of solutions

- How many solutions should you expect for each type of equation?
- Will there always be the same number of solutions for each type of equation?
- How can you determine the number of solutions from a graph?
- How can you determine the number of solutions using symbolic reasoning?

Suggested Solutions
Solving Equations

This project asks students to consolidate all of their knowledge about solving equations. Through their work on the project, students will review techniques for solving equations (both approximate and exact methods). They will also consider the number of solutions that an equation might have.

Suggested Timeline

You may want to complete this project as a class with different pairs or small groups of students considering different types of equations. Each group could prepare a report that addresses the question for the group's equation type. You might then spend time as a whole class looking for and discussing similarities and differences. Alternatively, you might want to let groups of students pick two or three types of equations to address.

Report Format

Part of the challenge of this project will be for students to organize their thinking well enough so they can convey it in a clear and concise manner. Struggling with this will help them find connections among solving different types of equations. You will need to be clear about what you expect from the students.

PRACTICING FOR STANDARDIZED TESTS

Practice Set

Solve each problem. Then record the letter that corresponds to the correct answer.

1. The endpoints of a diagonal of a square are $(-2, 2)$ and $(1, 5)$. What is the area of the square?

   (a) 3 **(b)** $3\sqrt{2}$ **(c)** 9 **(d)** 12 **(e)** 18

2. Frances can type 100 pages in h hours. At this rate, how many pages can she type in m minutes?

   (a) $\frac{mh}{60}$ **(b)** $\frac{60m}{h}$ **(c)** $\frac{100m}{60m}$ **(d)** $\frac{60h}{100m}$ **(e)** $\frac{100h}{60m}$

3. Find the measure to the nearest degree of the angle formed by the graph of $y = 1.5x$ $(x \geq 0)$ and the x-axis.

   (a) 51° **(b)** 56° **(c)** 59° **(d)** 60° **(e)** None of these

4. Which of the following is a solution to the equation $|3x - 6| = 3$?

   (a) -2 **(b)** -1 **(c)** 0 **(d)** 1 **(e)** 2

5. At a speed of 48 miles per hour, how many minutes will it take to drive 40 miles?

   (a) $\frac{5}{8}$ **(b)** $\frac{8}{5}$ **(c)** 32 **(d)** 50 **(e)** 1,920

6. If $a < 0$ and $b < 0$, which of the following must be less than 0?

   I. $a + b$ **II.** $a \cdot b$ **III.** $-\frac{a}{b}$

   (a) None of the above

   (b) I and II only

   (c) I and III only

   (d) II and III only

   (e) I, II, and III

7. If $\frac{n}{6} = 8$, what is the value of $\frac{n}{8}$?

   (a) 6 **(b)** $\frac{4}{3}$ **(c)** $\frac{3}{4}$ **(d)** $\frac{1}{6}$ **(e)** 2

8. For nonzero numbers x, y, and z, $3x = 4y$ and $12y = 5z$. What is $\frac{z}{x}$?

   (a) 4 **(b)** $\frac{16}{5}$ **(c)** $\frac{9}{5}$ **(d)** $\frac{6}{5}$ **(e)** $\frac{5}{16}$

9. On standardized tests like the ACT and SAT, every question is worth the same amount: one point. Assume there are five choices, A–E, for each item. Suppose you were bogged down on some questions and, with a minute left, you still have ten questions to answer. If you guess on each question and there is no guessing penalty, what is your expected score on the last ten items of the test?

(a) 1   (b) 2   (c) 3   (d) 4   (e) 5

10. The following sketch shows a shed wall. What is the area of the surface of this wall in square feet?

(a) 24

(b) 56

(c) 64

(d) 72

(e) None of these

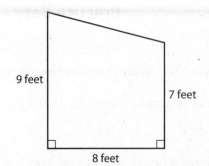

9 feet

7 feet

8 feet

TEST-TAKING TIP

Pay attention to units used in a problem.

Often the answer to a question must be in units different than those used in the statement of the problem. Be sure to read problems carefully and make the necessary conversions.

Example   Look back at Item 5. The speed is given in miles per hour, and the question asks for an answer in minutes. First, determine the time it will take in hours and then do the necessary conversion. Since $t = \frac{d}{r}$, $d = 40$ miles and $r = 48$ mph, you have $t = \frac{40}{48}$ hours. But $\frac{40}{48}$ hours $= \frac{40}{48}$ hours $\cdot \frac{60 \text{ min}}{1 \text{ hour}} = \frac{2{,}400}{48}$ min, or 50 minutes. So, the correct answer is (d).

Find, if possible, another test item in the practice set for which this strategy might be helpful.

Polynomial and Rational Functions

√ **1.** One factor of $16x^3 - 4x$ is:

A. $4x - 1$

B. $2x + 1$

C. $x + 4$

D. $2x - 4$

E. None of these

√ **2.** For which value of a will the equation $ax^2 + 8x = 4$ have no real number solutions?

A. $a = -5$

B. $a = -4$

C. $a = 0$

D. $a = 4$

E. $a = 5$

√ **3.** Which of the following is a function rule for a quadratic function with a vertex at (a, b)?

A. $y = (x - a)^2 + b$

B. $y = (x + a)^2 + b$

C. $y = (x - a)^2 - b$

D. $y = (x - b)^2 + a$

E. $y = (x + b)^2 - a$

4. The graph of $y = \frac{x^2 + ax}{x^2 - a^2}$ has a vertical asymptote at:

Skip
Am2

A. $y = 0$

B. $y = a$

C. $x = 0$

D. $x = a$

E. $x = -a$

5. If $a > 0$, which of the following is a possible function rule for the following graph?

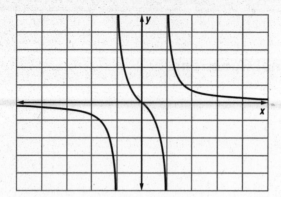

A. $f(x) = \dfrac{x + a}{x(x - a)}$

B. $f(x) = \dfrac{(x + a)(x - a)}{x}$

C. $f(x) = \dfrac{x - a}{x(x + a)}$

D. $f(x) = \dfrac{x}{(x + a)(x - a)}$

E. $f(x) = \dfrac{-x}{(x + a)(x - a)}$

6. Consider a polynomial with factored form $y = k(x + a)^2 (x - b)(x + c)$, where a, b, and c are positive, k is negative, and $a < c$. Sketch a possible graph of this polynomial. Explain each aspect of the graph.

7. Consider the following rational function: $y = \dfrac{(2x + 1)(x - 2)(x - 5)}{x^2 + x - 6}$.

  a. Identify any zeroes.

  b. Identify the y-intercept.

  c. Identify any vertical asymptotes or explain why it does not have any.

  d. Identify any horizontal asymptotes or explain why it does not have any.

  e. Find approximate values for any local or absolute maxima or minima.

8. The polynomial $f(x)$ has degree three, has zeroes of -2, 3, and 5, and $f(7) < 0$.

  a. Sketch a possible graph of $f(x)$.

  b. Write a possible function rule for $f(x)$.

  c. Is the function rule that you wrote in Part b the only one that satisfies all of the given conditions? Explain.

9. Research has shown that the daily total production costs for a certain brand of tent, which include materials, labor, and fixed expenses, can be modeled by the function $C(x) = 5x^2 + 18x + 1,500$, where x is the number of tents produced.

    a. Write a function rule that relates the production cost per tent to the number of tents produced.

    b. Does the graph of the cost-per-tent function in Part a have any asymptotes? If so, describe the location of the asymptotes and the meaning for this context.

    c. If you wished to have the lowest production cost per tent, how many tents should you produce each day?

10. Find all solutions to each equation. If the solutions are non-real complex numbers, give the solution in the form $a + bi$.

    a. $(x + 5)(x + 7) = 8$

    b. $(x - 14)^2 + 10 = 36$

    c. $3x^2 + 9x + 30 = 0$

    d. $2x^3 - 5x^2 + 3x = 0$

11. For each expression, write an equivalent expression in standard polynomial form.

    a. $(7x^3 - 6x + 4)(2x^2 - 7)$

    b. $(3x^3 + 4x^2 + 5) + (-3x^3 + x^2 - 1)$

    c. $(4x^3 + 5x - 2) - (x^4 - 7x + 5)$

12. Write each expression in an equivalent form as a single algebraic fraction. Then simplify the result as much as possible.

    a. $\dfrac{2x}{x + 2} \div \dfrac{x^2}{2x + 4}$

    b. $\dfrac{3x + 1}{5} + \dfrac{x + 4}{x}$

pgs 66 to 70 good for someone skipping AMZ

Circles and Circular Functions

1. In the diagram below, $\overline{AY}$ is tangent to the circle with center O, $\overline{XB}$ is tangent to the circle with center M, and $\overline{XY}$ is tangent to both circles. The radius of the circle with center O is 6 cm and the radius of the other circle is 3 cm. Which of the following is true?

    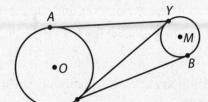

    A. $AY = XB > XY$

    B. $AY = XY > XB$

    C. $XY = XB < AY$

    D. $XY = XB = AY$

    E. None of the above statements are true.

2. In a circle with diameter 10 cm, $\overline{AB}$ is a chord with length 6 cm. How far is $\overline{AB}$ from the center of the circle?

    A. 2 cm

    B. 3 cm

    C. 4 cm

    D. 6 cm

    E. 8 cm

3. In a circle with center O, $\angle AOC$ is a central angle, $\angle ABC$ is an inscribed angle, and $AB = BC$. If $m\angle ABC = x°$, find the measure of $\overset{\frown}{AB}$.

    A. $2x°$

    B. $360° - 2x°$

    C. $360° - x°$

    D. $180° - \frac{x°}{2}$

    E. $180° - x°$

4. A wheel with radius 9 inches is attached by a belt to a wheel with radius 3 inches. If the larger wheel is turning at a rate of 4 revolutions per minute, what is the linear velocity of the smaller wheel?

    A. $\frac{4}{3}$ revolutions per minute

    B. 12 revolutions per minute

    C. 24π inches per minute

    D. 72π inches per minute

    E. 96π inches per minute

5. If $\cos \theta = x$, then which of the following is *not* true?

 A. $\cos (\theta + 2\pi) = x$

 B. $\cos (\theta - 2\pi) = -x$

 C. $\cos (-\theta) = x$

 D. $\cos (\pi - \theta) = -x$

 E. $\cos (\pi + \theta) = -x$

6. In the diagram below, the circles with centers M and P are congruent and $\overset{\frown}{AB} \cong \overset{\frown}{CD}$. Prove that quadrilateral *MAPD* is a parallelogram.

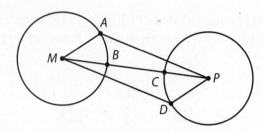

7. Quadrilateral *ABCD* is circumscribed around a circle with center *O*. Prove that $AB + CD = AD + BC$.

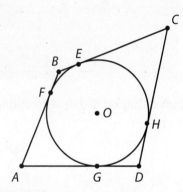

8. In the diagram below, points B and C are on a circle with center O, $\overline{AB}$ and $\overline{AC}$ are tangent to the circle, and m$\angle BOC = 146°$. Find the following lengths and measures.

 a. m$\angle A$

 b. m$\overset{\frown}{BC}$

 c. m$\angle BDC$

 d. m$\overset{\frown}{BDC}$

 e. If $AB = 15$ cm, find the radius of the circle.

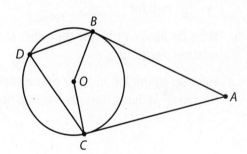

9. Audio CDs spin faster when they are reading data from near the center of the disc than they do when they are reading data near the outside edge of the disc. Suppose that when reading data that is 2.5 cm from the center of the disc, the disc spins at a rate of 8.3 revolutions per second.

 a. What is the angular velocity of the disc in degrees per second?

 b. What is the angular velocity of the disc in radian per second?

 c. What is the linear velocity, in meters per second, of this portion of the disc?

 d. Points near the outside edge of the disc are 6 cm from the center of the disc. How fast (revolutions per second) should the disc spin when reading data on the outside edge in order for that portion of the disc to have a linear velocity of 1.3 meters per second?

10. Suppose that a water wheel is mounted so that half the wheel is under the water. The wheel has a radius of 10 feet and turns counterclockwise. Bucket 1 has a starting position as shown in the diagram below.

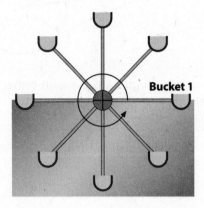

 a. Identify the letter of the location of Bucket 1 that corresponds with each amount of turn from the starting position.

    i. 300° _____

    ii. 540° _____

    iii. $\frac{3\pi}{2}$ radians _____

    iv. $\frac{\pi}{3}$ radians _____

    v. $\frac{11\pi}{6}$ radians _____

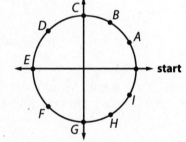

 b. How far above or below the water is Bucket 1 if the wheel has turned 150° from its starting position?

 c. How far to the left or right of the vertical axis of the wheel is Bucket 1 if the wheel has turned $\frac{5\pi}{4}$ radians from its starting position?

11. Over the past several years, the use of wind turbines to produce energy has increased. Consider a wind turbine like the one pictured here. The tower is 45 meters tall and the length of each blade is 20 meters. Assume that the blade is moving at one rotation per second.

a. Complete a table of values for the time x and height y above the ground of the endpoint of a blade that begins pointing directly to the right and begins moving in the upward direction.

Time (in seconds)	Height Above Ground (in meters)
0	
$\frac{1}{4}$	
$\frac{1}{2}$	
$\frac{3}{4}$	
1	

b. Use the data pairs in Part a to sketch a graph of the height above the ground y as a function of the time x for 3 rotations.

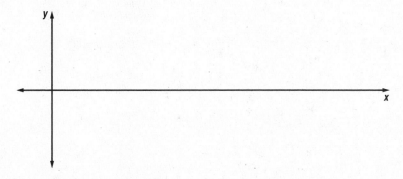

c. Write a function rule for the graph in Part b.

Suppose the amount of power P generated by this wind turbine is modeled by the equation $P = 7.9w^3$, where w is the wind velocity in kilometers per hour (km/hr) and power is measured in watts.

d. What wind speed will result in the production of 200,000 watts of power?

e. Suppose that the wind on one day was twice as fast as it was on the previous day. If the wind speed does not exceed the rated maximum for the turbine and all other conditions were the same, what was the relationship between the power produced on those two days?

12. One model of roto tiller has a forward speed of 44 feet per minute when the engine drive shaft has angular velocity of 3,000 rpm.

   a. The tiller assembly turns at 146 revolutions per minute. How many tilling cycles (revolutions) occur in each foot of a garden?

   b. The wheels on the tiller are 14 inches in diameter. What is the angular velocity of the wheels (in revolutions per minute)?

   c. What is the relationship between the angular velocities of the engine drive shaft v_D and the wheels v_W?

Recursion and Iteration

1. The population of fish in a lake at the end of each month can be modeled by the recursive function $P_n = 0.84P_{n-1} + 800$. If none of the conditions change, what will be the approximate long-term population of fish in the lake?

   A. 800 fish

   B. 952 fish

   C. 1,472 fish

   D. 5,000 fish

   E. There is not enough information to determine the long-term population of fish in the lake.

2. What is the value of U_{75} in the sequence defined by $U_n = U_{n-1} + 6$, $U_0 = 12$?

   A. 93

   B. 456

   C. 462

   D. 894

   E. 906

3. Find the sum, to the nearest hundredth, of the first twelve terms of the sequence defined by $A_n = 1.02A_{n-1}$, $A_0 = 1,250$.

   A. 1,554.22

   B. 1,585.30

   C. 15,300.00

   D. 16,765.11

   E. 18,350.41

4. Which type of function will best model the following table of values?

x	1	2	3	4	5	6	7
f(x)	15	40	75	120	175	240	315

   A. Linear

   B. Quadratic

   C. Cubic

   D. Exponential

5. Suppose that the nth term in a sequence is given by the function formula $f(n) = 8n + 5$. Which of the following is a correct recursive formula for the sequence?

A. $U_n = 8U_{n-1} + 5, U_0 = 0$

B. $U_n = U_{n-1} + 5, U_0 = 8$

C. $U_n = U_{n-1} + 8, U_0 = 5$

D. $U_n = 8U_{n-1}, U_0 = 5$

E. $U_n = 5U_{n-1} + 5, U_0 = 8$

6. Eva has a credit card balance of $2,528. Since this balance is more than one month old, the credit card company adds an interest charge each month until it is paid in full. The annual interest rate on this balance is 21%. Suppose that Eva makes monthly payments of $200 and does not make any additional charges to this card.

a. What is the monthly interest rate for this balance?

b. Write a recursive formula that can be used to find the credit card balance at the end of each month.

c. Complete the table below indicating the balance after each of the following number of months.

Number of Months	1	2	3	4
Credit Card Balance (in dollars)				

d. Is the sequence of credit card balances in the table above arithmetic, geometric, or neither? Explain your reasoning.

e. How many months will it take her to reach a zero balance?

f. How much interest will Eva have paid when she reaches a zero balance?

7. Suppose that Mark takes a part-time sales job from a company that says his initial monthly income will be $10, and this monthly income will double every month.

a. What kind of sequence (arithmetic or geometric) is formed by Mark's monthly salaries for the first year?

b. If Mark starts this job in January, what will his monthly salary be in December of that same year?

c. How much money total will Mark earn during his first year of work? Show your work.

d. Suppose that in January, Katie takes a different part-time job and is told that her starting salary will be $250 per month for the first month. Her salary will then increase by $25 per month. How much money total will Katie earn during the first year of work?

e. Write an inequality whose solution would answer the question: If Mark and Katie both start their jobs at the same time, how many months will it take before Mark's monthly salary is greater than Katie's monthly salary?

8. Consider the function $g(x) = 0.5x + 1$.

   a. Iterate the function starting with $x = 6$. Write the results of your iteration in the table below.

x	g(x)
6	

   b. Write a recursive formula using U_n and U_{n-1} that will produce the same sequence of values as the function iteration in Part a.

   c. Graphically iterate this function beginning at $x = 6$.

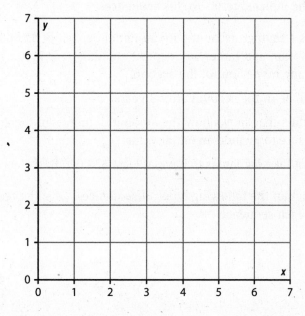

   d. Find the fixed point for this function iteration. Then indicate if the fixed point is attracting, repelling, or neither. Explain your reasoning.

   e. Explain how you can tell if the fixed point of a linear function is attracting or repelling from the symbolic form of the function.

9. Suppose that approximately 5% of the trees in a forest die each year due to weather and disease-related conditions. In a particular region of a forest, there are currently 5,000 trees. The forestry company has plans to cut down 200 trees each year.

   a. How many trees will be in this section of the forest after 5 years?

   b. Write a recursive formula that represents this situation. Be sure to specify the initial value.

   c. How many years will it be before there are fewer than 1,000 trees left in this section of forest?

   d. If the forest company continues to cut down 200 trees a year, how many trees should the company plant each year in order for there to be 5,000 trees in the forest at the end of each year?

10. Consider the two sequences below.

    a. 64, 96, 144, 216, ... , 1,640.25

        i. Determine if the sequence is arithmetic or geometric. Explain how you know.

        ii. Find a recursive formula *and* a function formula for this sequence.

          Recursive Formula:

          Function Formula:

        iii. If $t_0 = 64$, for what value of n is $t_n = 1,640.25$?

    b. 11, 16, 21, 26, ... , 106

        i. Determine if the sequence is arithmetic or geometric. Explain how you know.

        ii. Find a recursive formula *and* a function formula for this sequence.

          Recursive Formula:

          Function Formula:

        iii. Find the sum of the indicted terms in this sequence.

11. Suppose that James opens a savings account with an initial deposit of $2,000. The account will earn 7% interest each year, and James will deposit an additional $600 each year. Assume that James does not take any money out of the account.

    a. How much money will be in the account after 3 years?

    b. Write a recursive formula that shows how the amount of money in the account changes from year to year. Be sure to include an initial value.

    c. How many years will it take for James to have at least $20,000 in the account?

12. Describe the pattern in each of the following types of sequences. Give the recursive formula and function formula for each sequence.

    a. Arithmetic Sequence

    b. Geometric Sequence

Inverse Functions

1. If $f(x) = 3x - 12$, evaluate $f^{-1}(24)$.
   A. $\frac{1}{60}$
   B. 12
   C. 24
   D. 28
   E. 60

2. If $\log y = 4x - 3$, then y is:
   A. $10^{4x} - 3$
   B. $4 \cdot 10^{x-3}$
   C. $0.1 \cdot 10^x$
   D. $0.75 \cdot 10^x$
   E. $10^{4x} \cdot 10^{-3}$

3. If $12 = 4.16^x$, then x is:
   A. $\log 12 - \log 4.16$
   B. $\frac{\log 12}{\log 4.16}$
   C. $\log \frac{12}{4.16}$
   D. $(\log 12)(\log 4.16)$
   E. $\frac{\log 4.16}{\log 12}$

4. Which of the following is the solution to $\sin^{-1}\left(\sin\left(\frac{4\pi}{3}\right)\right)$?
   A. $\frac{4\pi}{3}$
   B. $-\frac{4\pi}{3}$
   C. $\frac{\pi}{3}$
   D. $\frac{4\pi}{3}$ and $-\frac{\pi}{3}$
   E. $-\frac{\pi}{3}$

5. If $1{,}000 < A < 10{,}000$, which of the following are true statements?
   I. $\log (A^2) = 2 \log A$
   II. $6 < \log (A^2) < 8$
   III. $9 < \log (A^2) < 16$
   A. I only
   B. II only
   C. III only
   D. I and II only
   E. I and III only

6. Find all the solutions to each equation.

  a. $10^{x+4} = 385$

  b. $2(6^{3x}) = 3{,}192$

  c. $\log 4x = 2.4$

  d. $2 \cos x = \sqrt{3}$ $\Big)$ same

  e. $\sin x + 4 = 2.75$

7. The amount of power $P(t)$ in watts available to a satellite is a function of time t in days since the satellite was put into orbit and is given by $P(t) = 50(0.996^t)$.

  a. How much power will be available to the satellite after 100 days?

  b. Explain what $P^{-1}(25) = 173$ tells you about the power supply in this satellite.

  c. The equipment on board requires 9 watts of power to operate properly. For how many days will the satellite operate properly?

8. Determine whether each of the following functions has an inverse. If it does have an inverse, find an algebraic rule for the inverse. If it does not have an inverse, explain why.

  a. $y = \frac{x}{5} + 8$

  b.

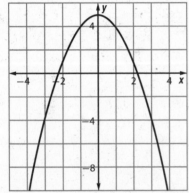

9. Suppose that the population of wolves in a study region is predicted by the function $f(t) = 30 \sin t + 80$, where t is time in years since January 2008.

  a. What are the predicted maximum and minimum populations? When do they first occur after 2008?

  b. Find all the times that the predicted wolf population will be 100.

10. Determine whether each statement is true or false. In each case, explain your reasoning.

  a. $\log (10^{x+2}) = 10^{x+2}$

  b. $\log \left(\frac{100}{x}\right) = 2 - \log x$

  c. $\log (10x^3) = 3 + 3 \log x$

  d. $10^{\log x} = x$

Solutions

Polynomial and Rational Functions

1. B

2. A

3. A

4. D

5. D

6. This is a fourth-degree polynomial with a negative leading coefficient. Therefore, the function values approach negative infinity as x approaches both negative and positive infinity. The zeroes of the polynomial are $-a$ (twice), b, and $-c$, which are negative, positive, and negative, respectively, and $-a > -c$. The graph has two relative maximum points and one relative minimum point. The relative minimum is at $(-a, 0)$.

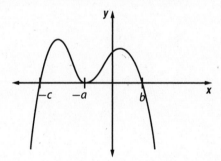

7. a. $x = -\frac{1}{2}$ and $x = 5$

b. The y-intercept is $\left(0, -\frac{5}{3}\right)$.

c. There is a vertical asymptote at $x = -3$.

d. There are no horizontal asymptotes because the degree of the numerator is greater than the degree of the denominator. This means that as $x \to \infty$, $y \to \infty$, and as $x \to -\infty$, $y \to -\infty$.

e. There is a local minimum at about $(1.47, -3.11)$.
There is a local maximum at about $(-7.47, -38.89)$.

8. a. One possible graph is shown below.

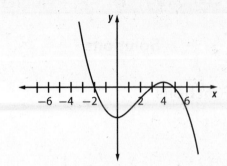

b. Rules may vary. A correct rule will be of the form $f(x) = k(x + 2)(x - 3)(x - 5)$, where $k < 0$.

c. There is more than one possible rule. Any value of $k < 0$ will give a polynomial that meets the constraints.

9. a. The production cost per tent is $P(x) = \dfrac{5x^2 + 18x + 1{,}500}{x}$.

b. There is a vertical asymptote at $x = 0$. This indicates that producing fewer units gets very costly. (Technically, this is a discrete context and you cannot produce fractions of tents.) There are no horizontal asymptotes.

c. The local minimum is at about (17.32, 191.21). Thus, they should produce 17 tents per day at a cost of $191.21 per tent.

10. a. $x = -9$ or $x = -3$

b. $x = 14 \pm \sqrt{26}$

c. $x = -\dfrac{3}{2} \pm \dfrac{\sqrt{31}}{2}i$

d. $x = 0$, $x = 1$, or $x = \dfrac{3}{2}$

11. a. $14x^5 - 61x^3 + 8x^2 + 42x - 28$
b. $5x^2 + 4$
c. $-x^4 + 4x^3 + 12x - 7$

12. a. $\dfrac{4}{x}$

b. $\dfrac{3x^2 + 6x + 20}{5x}$

Assessment Master

Circles and Circular Functions

1. D

2. C

3. E

4. D

5. B

6. Since the circles with centers M and P are congruent, they have the same radius. So, $MA = PD$. We know that $m\angle AMB = m\widehat{AB}$ and $m\angle CPD = m\widehat{CD}$ because $\angle AMB$ and $\angle CPD$ are central angles and so have the same measure as their intercepted arcs. We are given that $m\widehat{AB} = m\widehat{CD}$, so by substitution, $m\angle AMB = m\angle CPD$. If $m\angle AMB = m\angle CPD$, then $\overline{AM} \parallel \overline{PD}$ because $\angle AMB$ and $\angle CPD$ are alternate interior angles. If $\overline{AM} \parallel \overline{PD}$ and $AM = PD$, then $APDM$ is a parallelogram because there is one pair of opposite sides that are congruent and parallel.

   Another method would be to begin by using the SAS triangle congruence theorem to show that $\triangle AMP \cong \triangle DPM$. Then we know that both pairs of opposite sides congruent, and thus, $APDM$ is a parallelogram.

7. Since the tangent segments drawn to a circle from an exterior point are congruent, you know that:

   $BE = BF$
   $CE = CH$
   $DG = DH$
   $AG = AF$

   By the Addition Property of Equality:

   $BE + CE + DG + AG = BF + CH + DH + AF$

   By the Segment Addition Postulate:

   $BE + CE = BC$
   $DG + AG = AD$
   $BF + AF = AB$
   $CH + DH = CD$

   So, $BE + CE + DG + AG = BC + AD$ and $BF + AF + CH + DH = AB + CD$.
   By substitution, $BC + AD = AB + DC$.

8. a. $m\angle A = 360° - 90° - 90° - 146° = 34°$

b. $m\overset{\frown}{BC} = 146°$

c. $m\angle BDC = \frac{1}{2}(146°) = 73°$

d. $m\overset{\frown}{BDC} = 360° - 146° = 214°$

e. $\tan 17° = \frac{OB}{15}$

$OB = 15 \tan 17° \approx 4.6$ cm
The radius of the circle with center O is
approximately 4.6 cm.

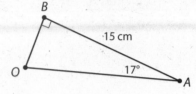

9. a. $(8.3)(360) = 2{,}988$ degrees per second

b. $(8.3)(2\pi) = 16.6\pi \approx 52.15$ radians per second

c. $(8.3)(5\pi) = 41.5\pi \approx 130.4$ cm per second $= 1.304$ meters per second

d. Let x be the revolutions per second.
Then $12\pi x = 130$, or $x = \frac{130}{12\pi} \approx 3.45$ revolutions per second.

10. a. **i.** H

ii. E

iii. G

iv. B

v. I

b. $10 \sin 150° = 10\left(\frac{1}{2}\right) = 5$ feet above the water

c. $10\left(\cos \frac{5\pi}{4}\right) \approx -7.07$, which is about 7.07 feet to the left of the vertical axis.

11. a.

Time (in seconds)	Height Above Ground (in meters)
0	45
$\frac{1}{4}$	65
$\frac{1}{2}$	45
$\frac{3}{4}$	25
1	45

b.

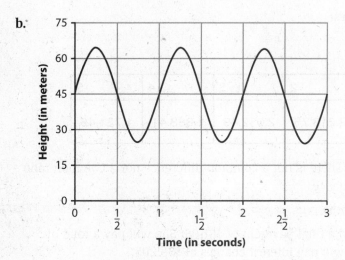

c. $y = 45 + 20 \sin 2\pi x$

d. $200{,}000 = 7.9w^3$

$$w^3 = \frac{200{,}000}{7.9} \approx 25{,}300$$

$$w \approx 29 \text{ km/hr}$$

e. Students may do this task a variety of ways. They may reason based on the fact that doubling the wind means the power is 2^3, or 8 times as great.

Students may reason as shown below.

$P_1 = 7.9w^3$ on the first day

$P_2 = 7.9(2w)^3$ on the second day

$\qquad = 7.9w^3(2^3)$

$\qquad = 8(7.9w^3)$

$P_2 = 8P_1$, so the power is 8 times as great.

12. a. $\dfrac{146 \text{ rpm}}{44 \text{ ft/min}} \approx 3.3$ tilling cycles per foot

b. Since the circumference of the wheels in feet is approximately 1.167π, the angular velocity of the wheels is $\dfrac{44 \text{ ft/min}}{1.167\pi \text{ ft/rev}} \approx 12.0$ rpm.

c. Since the engine shaft rotates at 3,000 rpm and the follower (the wheels) turn at 12 rpm, we have the following: 12 rpm ÷ 3,000 rpm = 0.004, so $v_w = 0.004v_D$.

Recursion and Iteration

1. D

2. C

3. D

4. B

5. C

6. **a.** $\frac{0.21}{12} = 0.0175$, or 1.75% monthly interest

   b. $U_n = 1.0175U_{n-1} - 200$, $U_0 = 2{,}528$

   c.

Number of Months	1	2	3	4	5
Credit Card Balance (in dollars)	2,372.24	2,213.75	2,052.49	1,888.41	1,721.46

   d. It is neither arithmetic nor geometric. There is not a common difference nor a common ratio between consecutive terms in the sequence.

   e. She will pay off the balance in 15 months.

   f. There will be 14 payments of $200 and a final payment of $81.08. She will pay a total of $200(14) + 81.08 = \$2{,}881.08$. So, she will pay interest charges of $353.08.

7. **a.** The monthly salaries will be a geometric sequence.

   b. His monthly salary in December would be $\$20{,}480 = 10(2^{11})$.

   c. $M_{12} = 10\left(\frac{2^{12} - 1}{2 - 1}\right) = \$40{,}950$

   d. $K_{12} = \frac{12(250 + 525)}{2} = 6(775) = \$4{,}650$

   e. $10(2^{n-1}) > 250 + 25(n - 1)$

8. a.

x	g(x)
6	4
4	3
3	2.5
2.5	2.25

b. $U_n = 0.5U_{n-1} + 1$, $U_0 = 6$

c.

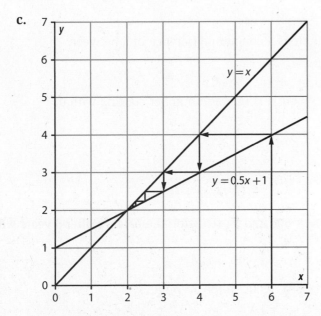

d. The fixed point is $(2, 2)$, which can be calculated by solving $x = 0.5x + 1$ for x. This is an attracting fixed point, approached more closely with each iteration.

e. If the absolute value of the slope is less than 1, the fixed point is attracting. If the absolute value of the slope is greater than 1, the fixed point is repelling.

9. a. Approximately 2,964 trees

b. $T_n = 0.95T_{n-1} - 200$, $T_0 = 5,000$

c. After 12 years, there will be approximately 863 trees left in the forest.

d. Since $0.05(5,000) = 250$, the company will need to replace these 250 trees that die and also the 200 it cuts down. So, the company needs to plant 450 trees each year.

10. a.   **i.** The sequence is geometric because each term is 1.5 times the preceding term.

     ii. Recursive Formula: $A_n = 1.5A_{n-1}, A_0 = 64$
         Function Formula: $A_n = 64(1.5^n)$, where n is the term number starting with 0

     iii. Students might use a calculator and the recursive formula to determine that $n = 8$. Symbolically, the solution is as follows:

$$1{,}640.25 = 64(1.5^n)$$

$$\frac{\log \frac{1{,}640.25}{64}}{\log 1.5} = n$$

$$n = 8$$

b.   **i.** The sequence is arithmetic because there is a common difference of 5 between consecutive terms.

     ii. Recursive Formula: $A_n = A_{n-1} + 5, A_0 = 11$
         Function Formula: $A_n = 5n + 11$, where n is the term number starting with 0

     iii. $106 = 5n + 11$
         $19 = n$
         So, there are 20 terms in the sequence.

$$S_{19} = \frac{20(11 + 106)}{2} = 1{,}170$$

11. a. Using the recursive formula $B_n = 1.07B_{n-1} + 600$ and a calculator, the balance after 3 years will be approximately \$4,379.

b. $B_n = 1.07B_{n-1} + 600, B_0 = 2{,}000$

c. It will take 15 years for James to have at least \$20,000 in the account.

12. a. An arithmetic sequence is a sequence whose consecutive terms increase or decrease by addition of a constant. If the constant difference is d, the recursive formula is $A_n = A_{n-1} + d$ and the function formula is $A_n = A_0 + nd$ or $A_n = A_1 + (n-1)d$, which is a linear function.

b. A geometric sequence is a sequence in which each term is a constant multiple of the previous one. If the common ratio is r, the recursive formula is $A_n = rA_{n-1}$ and the function formula is $A_n = A_0 r^n$ or $A_n = A_1 r^{n-1}$.

Inverse Functions

1. B

2. E

3. B

4. E

5. D

6. **a.** $x + 4 = \log 385$
$$x = -4 + \log 385$$
$$x \approx -1.4$$

b. $6^{3x} = 1{,}596$
$$3x \log 6 = \log 1{,}596$$
$$3x = \frac{\log 1{,}596}{\log 6} \approx 4.116$$
$$x \approx 1.37$$

c. $10^{2.4} = 4x$
$$x = \frac{10^{2.4}}{4} \approx 62.8$$

d. $\cos x = \frac{\sqrt{3}}{2}$
Solution in radians:
$$x = \frac{\pi}{6} + 2\pi n, \text{ for any integer } n$$
$$x = -\frac{\pi}{6} + 2\pi n, \text{ for any integer } n$$

Solution in degrees:
$$x = 30° + 360°n, \text{ for any integer } n$$
$$x = -30° + 360°n, \text{ for any integer } n$$

e. $\sin x = -1.25$
No solutions exist.

7. **a.** $P(100) = 50(0.996^{100}) \approx 33.5$ watts

b. After 173 days, the available power will be 25 watts.

c. $9 = 50(0.996^t)$
$$\frac{9}{50} = 0.996^t$$
$$t = \frac{\log \frac{9}{50}}{\log 0.996} \approx 427.8 \text{ days}$$
The satellite will operate for approximately 427.8 days.

8. **a.** The function has an inverse.

   The rule for the inverse is $y = 5(x - 8) = 5x - 40$.

   b. The function does not have an inverse because there are different x values that give the same y value. For example, $f(1) = f(-1) = 4$. This means it is not clear to what $f^{-1}(4)$ should be equal.

9. **a.** The maximum population is 110 wolves and will occur approximately 1.57 years after January 2008, or during June of 2009.

   The minimum population is 50 wolves and will occur approximately 4.7 years after January 2008, or during August 2012.

   b. $30 \sin t + 80 = 100$

   $\sin t = \frac{2}{3}$

   $t \approx 0.73$

   There will be 100 wolves when $t \approx 0.73 + 2\pi n$, for any integer n, and when $t \approx 2.41 + 2\pi n$, for any integer n.

10. **a.** False: $\log (10^{x+2}) = x + 2$, not 10^{x+2}

    b. True: $\log \left(\frac{100}{x} \right) = \log 100 - \log x = 2 - \log x$

    c. False: $\log (10x^3) = \log 10 + \log x^3 = 1 + 3 \log x$

    d. True: $\log x$ is the power you can raise 10 to, to get x, thus $10^{\log x} = x$.

Technological Tools and Mathematics

As you engaged in the learning and doing of mathematics over the last year, you made use of a variety of technological tools for a variety of purposes. During the year, you likely used some or all of the following tools: calculators, CAS, spreadsheets, interactive geometry software, and statistics and data analysis software. As you learn to make use of new tools, it is helpful to identify the types of tasks for which each tool is best suited. It is also important to reflect on why and when you are using each tool.

1. Make a list of the all the different technology tools that you have used this year while you were learning and doing mathematics. For each tool that you have used, briefly discuss what you learned to do with that tool.

2. Technological tools can be used in many different ways, some of which are:
   - Assisting you in developing new ideas
   - Supporting you in accurately completing a task by saving time
   - Allowing you to do something you would not have been able to do without the use of technology
   - Checking your work

   Briefly describe an instance in which you used technology in each of these four ways. Describe the task and describe what you did with the technology and how it helped in your learning or problem solving.

3. Now that you have thought about what technological tools you know how to use and you have reviewed some of the ways that you used them during this year, you need to think about decisions that you have or will make about using technology. The list below contains problems that you may or may not have done.

Unit 1 Lesson 5 Task 4	Unit 6 Lesson 1 On Your Own Task 27
Unit 2 Lesson 1 On Your Own Task 20	Unit 6 Lesson 2 On Your Own Task 12
Unit 2 Lesson 2 On Your Own Task 31	Unit 6 Lesson 2 On Your Own Task 15
Unit 3 Lesson 2 Investigation 1 Problem 5	Unit 7 Lesson 1 On Your Own Task 2
Unit 3 Lesson 2 On Your Own Task 34	Unit 7 Lesson 1 On Your Own Task 15
Unit 3 Lesson 3 Problem 7	Unit 7 Lesson 2 On Your Own Task 6
Unit 4 Lesson 2 On Your Own Task 6	Unit 7 Lesson 3 On Your Own Task 5
Unit 5 Lesson 1 On Your Own Task 18	Unit 8 Lesson 2 On Your Own Task 10
	Unit 8 Lesson 3 On Your Own Task 9

Choose five of the problems and discuss whether or not you would use technology while working on the problem and how you would use it or why you would not use it. The problems that you choose should make use of at least two different technological tools.

You might find it helpful to consider the following questions as you write your answer to this part of the project:

- How do you decide when you will use technology and what technology you will use?

- Are there times when you will use technology even though you can complete the task without the use of technology?

- Why do you choose to use technology in those instances?

4. Discuss what you think are some advantages and disadvantages of using technology when you are learning and doing mathematics. Whenever possible, support your comments with specific examples.

Suggested Solutions
Technological Tools and Mathematics

As students progressed through the first three courses of *Core-Plus Mathematics*, they learned to use a variety of technological tools. This project asks students to take a step back and reflect on their individual use of technology. Students are asked to summarize how and when they used technology. This is important because once they are out of mathematics classes, they will have to decide when to make use of technology and what would be the best technology to use.

Students may not have thought about when they use technology or what technology they choose to use for any given problem. If they are having difficulty reflecting on their use of technology, you may wish to have a short class discussion about decision-making around the use of technology.

Timeline

The first two parts of this project are best completed by pairs of students. The last two parts ask students to reflect on their own decision-making about using technology and should be completed individually by students. Students will need at least a week to complete this project. You may want to have students peer-edit the first draft of the projects and then have them revise their work and turn it into you.

Report Format

You will want to stress to your students that they are being asked to find specific examples to discuss in each part of this project. In order for them to do this, they will need to look back over their work from the entire year and review their use of technology.

Some students may find it easier to complete the four parts of the project as separate small reports. That is fine. But you may have other students who think it is easier to integrate the parts and consider their use of technology more holistically. You will need to be clear about your expectations.

PROJECT

Mathematical Reasoning and Proof

The first unit of Course 3 of *Core-Plus Mathematics* is titled *Reasoning and Proof*. While working on this unit, you formalized some of your previous work related to mathematical reasoning and laid a foundation for your future use of mathematical reasoning and proof. This project asks you to look back over your work from the entire year and reflect on your developing ability to make reasoning and proof an integral part of your mathematical thinking. For this project, you should write one paper that addresses all of the following.

1. Mathematical reasoning and proof is a process and is often characterized by the three phases of exploring a situation, developing a conjecture, and providing reasoning to show that your conjecture is true or false. In your own words, explain what each of these phases entails and how they work together to establish mathematical ideas. As you write this explanation, you should also consider the following questions.

   - In what ways do you use inductive reasoning in mathematics?

   - In what ways do you use deductive reasoning in mathematics?

   - What are the fundamental tools that you use in mathematical reasoning and proof?

   - How can you prove that something is not true in mathematics?

   - How sure are you of your conclusions in mathematics?

2. Look back over the work that you have completed this year. Identify one mathematics result that can be proven using two different methods of proofs. State the result and then give two different proofs of the result. The proofs you give should utilize different methods of proof. Which of the proofs do you like better? Why?

3. Identify one method of proof that you found especially helpful this year. Give at least two examples of how you used that proof technique in your mathematical work this year.

4. Throughout the year, you experienced ways that algebraic and geometric reasoning support each other. Although algebra and geometry are often seen as distinct parts of mathematics, reasoning in one area can often help develop knowledge in the other area.

   a. Identify an algebraic result that was proved using reasoning that was primarily geometric. Then provide a proof of the result.

   b. Identify a geometric result that was proved using reasoning that was primarily algebraic. Then provide a proof of the result.

5. In what way has your understanding of and ability to engage in mathematical proof and reasoning changed since the beginning of the year? What challenges do you still face in relation to mathematical proof and reasoning?

Copyright © Glencoe/McGraw-Hill, a division of The McGraw-Hill Companies, Inc.

PROJECT

Suggested Solutions
Mathematical Reasoning and Proof

One of the major goals of Course 3 was to help students understand the need for mathematical reasoning and to formalize the reasoning and proof in which they have been engaging during the past two years. While completing this project, students will look back over the reasoning and proof work that they have completed this year and identify examples of proofs that employ different proof methods. The goal of this project is not to develop further ability in writing proof but rather to have students take a step back and think more globally about the process of mathematical reasoning and proof. Since this is the goal, it is acceptable for students to find proofs that they have already written to use as examples in this project. However, you should encourage students to review each proof to see if they can improve upon what they did previously rather than just copying their work from earlier in the year.

Timeline

Students will probably need two weeks to complete this project. Since parts of the project ask students to reflect on their own experiences with proof and reasoning, it is best completed by individual students. After giving students a few days to begin their work on this project, it might be helpful to have a short class discussion about the different methods of proof that they have used. You want to be sure that students are focusing on methods of proof and not forms used to communicate their proofs (i.e., writing the proof in a paragraph or in two columns). The methods that you and your students might identify include synthetic proof, coordinate proof, indirect proof, proof by algebraic reasoning, and proof by cases. While not everyone would agree that these are all different methods of proof, for these students, it is probably beneficial to think of them as different so that they can better identify their options when presented with a statement to prove or disprove.

   Before students prepare their final draft, you may wish to have them exchange work and provide feedback to each other about what they have written. They can then revise their work and submit it to you.

Report Format

Students should be able to write one cohesive paper that addresses all of the parts of this project. You should be sure that your students know what your expectations are regarding the final preparation of their work on this project.

PROJECT

Mathematical Habits of Mind

In this course, you have continued to learn important mathematical concepts and methods, and you have gained valuable experience in thinking mathematically. Look back over the mathematical work you completed in Units 5–8 of Course 3 and consider some of the mathematical thinking you did. In particular, think about times when you did each of the following:

a. Search for and explain patterns;

b. Formulate or find a mathematical model;

c. Make and check conjectures;

d. Describe and use an algorithm;

e. Visualize;

f. Simulate a situation;

g. Predict;

h. Make connections—between mathematics and the real world and within mathematics itself;

i. Use a variety of representations for the same idea—like tables, graphs, function rules, equations, words, and physical models;

j. Reason from definitions and given or assumed facts.

Write a report that identifies at least two instances when you used each type of mathematical thinking. Give specific examples and describe how that type of thinking helped you discover important mathematical ideas that helped you analyze a situation.

PROJECT

Suggested Solutions
Mathematical Habits of Mind

Have students consider Units 5–8 and look for examples of the mathematical thinking in each of the habits of mind. Be certain that students include at least two instances and describe how that type of thinking helped them discover mathematical ideas or helped them analyze a situation. These habits of mind permeated the curriculum; therefore, the following solutions are merely suggestions of possible contexts from which students might draw.

Possible responses:

a. Search for and explain patterns—In Unit 5, students looked for patterns in the number of maximum and minimum points in graphs of polynomial functions and in how the coefficients of the function rules and the graphs polynomial function rules are related. Students also searched for and explained patterns when they determined the characteristics of algebraic and geometric sequences in Unit 7.

b. Formulate or find a mathematical model—Throughout Unit 5, students formulated and used mathematical models to represent total expenses, income and profit and expenses, income and profit per ticket sold. In Unit 6, they found mathematical models for circular motion and for periodic phenomenon. In Unit 7, students modeled fish pond population and bacteria growth using recursive formulas.

c. Make and check conjectures—In Unit 6, students made and checked several different conjectures about the relationship between a chord and the radius of the circle perpendicular to the chord, and between the measures of angles and intercepted arcs. In Unit 7, students conjectured about and then verified how the initial population, restocking amount, or annual decrease rate affects the long term population of a fish pond. They also conjectured about the properties of a finite differences table for a cubic polynomial. In Unit 7, students also made and checked conjectures about when linear function iteration will converge and when it will grow without bound.

d. Describe and use an algorithm—In Unit 5, students used an algorithm to change a quadratic expression in standard form into a quadratic expression in vertex form. Students used algorithms in Unit 7 when they determined whether a sequence is modeled by a polynomial of degree n. They also used algorithms to code and decode message in Unit 8.

e. Visualize—In Unit 5, students used visualization to help them identify key points to use for curve fitting. They also used visualization when using algebra tiles to help them understand completing the square. In Unit 6, students used visualization to help them identify patterns associated with circular motion. In Unit 7, visualization helped students explore problems about Sierpinski carpet area and the Koch snowflake.

f. Simulate a situation—In Unit 6, students used a computer drawing to simulate and explore horizontal danger areas. In Unit 7, students used recursive functions to simulate change in population in a fish pond.

g. Predict—Throughout all four units, students used algebraic function rules to make predictions. In particular, the predicted profit, expenses, and income in Unit 5, the long-term behavior of populations in Unit 6, and depth of water in a harbor in Unit 8.

h. Make connections—between mathematics and the real world and within mathematics itself— Students saw connections between mathematics and the real world throughout all four of the units in the second half of Course 3. In particular, they saw the following: Unit 5: income, expenses, and profit for a business are represented by polynomial and rational functions; Unit 6: motion of gears and pulleys are analyzed using angular velocity and linear velocity; Unit 7: loan and credit card balances are analyzed using recursive functions and spreadsheets; Unit 8: text messaging is related to coding and decoding and inverse function, sound waves and other periodic phenomenon are connected to trigonometric functions.

  Connections between parts of mathematics were also explored in these units. For example, in Unit 5, students explored connections between different forms of a quadratic expression and the graph of the related quadratic function. In Unit 7, they saw connections between arithmetic sequences and linear functions and between geometric sequences and exponential functions.

i. Use a variety of representations for the same idea—like tables, graphs, function rules, equations, words and physical models—Throughout Unit 5, students used tables, equations, words, and graphs to represent situations related to income, expenses, and profit. In Unit 7, students used *NOW-NEXT*, subscript, and function notation to show change from one year to the next or to represent a sequence of values.

j. Reason from definitions and given or assumed facts—Throughout Lesson 1 of Unit 6, students used definitions and given facts to prove theorems about chords in a circle and about relationships between angles measures and measure of intercepted arcs. In that same lesson, students also used theorems and given information to find the measures of specific angles or the lengths of specific segments. In Unit 8, students reasoned from the definition of logarithm and the properties of exponents to derive the properties of logarithms.

Assessment Master